ENGLISH MEDICINE

IN THE SEVENTEENTH CENTURY

English Medicine
in the Seventeenth Century

A.W. SLOAN

Emeritus Professor of Physiology
University of Cape Town

Durham Academic Press

First published in 1996 by
Durham Academic Press
1 Hutton Close
South Church
Bishop Auckland
Durham

ISBN 1-90083-800-1

Typeset by Carnegie Publishing, 18 Maynard St, Preston
Printed and bound by Bookcraft, Bath.

Contents

Illustrations

Preface

THE SEVENTEENTH CENTURY IN ENGLAND was a period of transition in medicine as well as in many other aspects of the life of the nation. In both the science and the practice of medicine earlier beliefs were challenged and, in some cases, replaced by new concepts, some of which are accepted today. English medicine was an integral part of European medicine but England contributed more to the fund of European medical knowledge in the seventeenth than in previous centuries.

In this book the pattern of English medicine is outlined and illustrated by brief biographies of some physicians. Some earlier medical beliefs and practices are described, which still influenced the practice of medicine in Stuart England and examples are given of the physicians' practice in the Stuart period. The principal advances in medical science – much more dramatic than in medical practice – are outlined. The professional activities of apothecaries, surgeons, and midwives are surveyed, as well as the domestic medicine practised by housewives, the contribution of the clergy, and the widespread, though illegal, practice by 'quacks'. Some of the infectious diseases, which were the main cause of death, are described and, finally, an attempt is made to sum up the foundations laid in the seventeenth century for the far greater advances made in the following centuries.

A select bibliography at the end of the book lists some of the key references, which have been published or reprinted in the twentieth century.

Most of the earlier writings are available in the Wellcome Historical Medical Library in London. Some of these and others are to be found in the British Library, the London Library, the University Libraries of Oxford, Glasgow, and Cape Town, the Libraries of the Royal Colleges of Physicians, of Surgeons, and of Obstetricians and Gynaecologists, and the Library of the Royal Society of Medicine. The author is grateful to the librarians of these institutions for giving him access to seventeenth–century and other medical literature.

Thanks are due especially to Mr Geoffrey Davenport, librarian of the Royal College of Physicians, for much useful information, to Major Charles O'Leary, Clerk of the Worshipful Society of Apothecaries of London, for information about early members of the Society, and to two general historians, Professor Nigel Worden and Dr Elizabeth van Heyningen, and two medical historians, Dr James MacGregor and Dr Peter Brain, for constructive criticism of the text. The late Dr Charles Newman, for seventeen years Harveian Librarian of the Royal College of Physicians of London, assisted in the preparation of a preliminary draft.

Dates of the more important publications are given in the text. Dates of birth and death are usually omitted from the narrative but, where known, will be found in the index. Dates are given New Style, the year beginning on 1 January.

The provenance of the illustrations is acknowledged in the legends.

The editors of the *South African Medical Journal* and the *Adler Museum Bulletin of the History of Medicine* (University of the Witwatersrand) have kindly granted me permission to include material from several papers I have published in these journals. The author is also indebted to his wife for assistance in compiling the index.

CHAPTER I

The Pattern of English Medicine

P RACTITIONERS OF MEDICINE occupied an important place in society
in the seventeenth century. In general the physicians were regarded as
gentlemen, the surgeons as craftsmen, and the apothecaries as merchants.
The physicians' fees were too high for any but the wealthy to pay, but
poor deserving patients might be treated *gratis* or for a greatly reduced fee.
More commonly the poor would rely on domestic remedies or consult
an apothecary.

Both in town and in the country most practitioners of medicine or
surgery, or of medicine and surgery, lacked academic training but had
served a course of apprenticeship (usually seven years) with a recognised
medical practitioner and then used the title 'surgeon-apothecary'. To
comply with the law they were required to obtain a licence to practise
from the bishop of the diocese or from the College of Physicians of
London, but many ignored this requirement. Most rural practitioners had
neither degree nor licence. The ecclesiastical licence might be little more
than a certificate of religious orthodoxy and loyalty to the Crown. Medical
graduates of Oxford or Cambridge were not required to be licensed except
in London and within seven miles of the city, where the licence would
be granted by the Bishop of London, the Dean of St Paul's or the College.
In 1600 London had about 50 physicians, 100 apothecaries, 100 surgeons, and 250 other medical practitioners, many with an ecclesiastical
licence.[1]

An annotated list of medical practitioners licensed in the diocese of
London from 1529 to 1725 includes 139 in the period 1601–1700.[2] No
such comprehensive survey has been made for the rest of the country but
a directory has been prepared of physicians practising outside London in
the period 1603–1643; in 1643 the ecclesiastical hierarchy which kept
records of licensed practitioners was abolished by Act of Parliament. Of
the 814 physicians on the list 635 had matriculated at a university but only
328 received a BA degree and only 246 proceeded to MD.[3]

Medical training

The formal education of a physician was effectively restricted to the universities of Oxford and Cambridge, in both of which the medical curriculum consisted of detailed study of the classics, with some anatomy but no other medical science. The professors were required to lecture 'in Hippocrates and Galen'[4] and at Oxford four lectures were to be on the dissected body of an executed criminal. At Cambridge this requirement was often ignored.

The Oxford curriculum required 4 years to become a Bachelor and 3 more to become a Master of Arts, 3 more for the degree of Bachelor of Medicine and 4 more to become a Doctor of Medicine, a total of 14 years. Cambridge required 6 years for the degree of Bachelor of Medicine and 5 more for the Doctorate. An Arts degree was not obligatory at Cambridge but most medical students had previously graduated in Arts. Both universities required a period of practice with an experienced medical practitioner before graduating as Doctor of Medicine.

Many students preferred to take their medical degree in a shorter time and with a more scientific approach at a good foreign medical school, such as Padua or Montpellier, and then pay for it to be 'incorporated' at Oxford or Cambridge. Most were satisfied to graduate BA or MA and then seek a licence to practise medicine or surgery or both. Some postgraduate medical training was offered as lectures by the College of Physicians, which was sometimes called the King's College or even the Royal College, though the designation, Royal, was granted only in 1851.[5]

The physician

In the seventeenth century the physician was the aristocrat of the medical profession, a scholar as well as a practitioner. After 1518, when it was founded, the leading physicians in London and its environs were usually Fellows of the College of Physicians, whose licence to practise was normally granted only to graduates of the universities of Oxford or Cambridge, although these graduates had often undertaken their medical training elsewhere. The holder of a Bachelor's degree could become a Licentiate but only a Doctor of Medicine could become a Fellow, or a Candidate (because the number of Fellows was limited). In 1599 the number of Fellows was restricted to thirty and the number of Candidates to six.[6]

In addition to the medical scientists, William Harvey (p. 12), Francis

Glisson (p. 16), and Thomas Willis (p.17), all of whom were successful physicians in London and closely associated with the College, the Fellows included Sir Theodore de Mayerne (p. 19), physician to King James I and King Charles I, Edmund Dickinson (p. 21), physician to Charles II and James II, Daniel Whistler, physician, mathematician, and a founder member of the Royal Society, and John Radcliffe, less scholarly but more wealthy than most of his colleagues. Thomas Sydenham (p. 22), commonly regarded as the greatest physician of the century, became a Licentiate in 1663 but never a Candidate or a Fellow. Charles Goodall, friend and colleague of Sydenham, became a Fellow of the College in 1680 and President in 1708. Probably the best known of the physicians who practised outside London was Sir Thomas Browne of Norwich (p. 31), who had studied at Oxford, Montpellier, Padua, and Leyden. He was elected an Honorary Fellow of the College of Physicians in 1664 but is best known for his *Religio medici* (1642), a philosophical treatise on theology. Some country practitioners left interesting records of their practice; among these were John Symcotts (p. 29) and Sir John Floyer (p. 33).

There were many unlicensed practitioners throughout the country but only in London did the College sue them for illegal practice, as it was entitled to do, and not all the prosecutions were successful because some defendants had friends in high places. As a rule only the more blatant charlatans were charged, although a new charter in 1617 'gave the president and censors the right to examine, survey, govern, correct and punish all physicians, practitioners of physic, apothecaries, druggists, distillers and so forth in London'.[7] In rural areas many clergymen practised medicine, although the College refused to license clergy.

After the Civil Wars and the Interregnum, during which the College had to maintain a low profile because of its royalist sympathies, its charter was amended and the amended version was approved by Charles II in 1663, but the new privileges which it claimed, including the sole right to license physicians throughout the country, were never confirmed by Parliament. In 1665 an attempt was made to create a 'Society of Chymical Physitians' in opposition to the College of Physicians but it failed to obtain a royal charter and dissolved after a few years.[8] The authority of the College waxed and waned with the authority of the Crown, so it was diminished by the end of the century. *The Decline of the Old Medical Regime in Stuart London* (1986), by H. J. Cook, describes not the decline of medicine, which showed some modest advance, but the decline in the authority of the College. The College, however, continued to regulate the professional behaviour of its Licentiates, Candidates, and Fellows. Charges of malpractice were investigated and the physician, if found guilty, was admonished or fined.

The apothecary

In 1605 the apothecaries in London were incorporated in the Grocers' Guild. In 1617, against considerable opposition from the grocers and from some apothecaries, they obtained a charter to form a separate body, the Worshipful Society of the Art and Mystery of the Apothecaries of the City of London, with the sole right to dispense and sell medicines in London and within seven miles of the city.[9] Practising apothecaries were incorporated as founder members but future candidates were to be examined by the Master and Wardens of the Society before admission to membership. The Society also had the duty to inspect the stock of individual apothecaries, destroy anything unsatisfactory, and punish the offender, though this did not annul the right of the College of Physicians to do this. On at least one occasion (in 1662) the President of the College of Physicians accompanied the representatives of the Society in their inspection.[10] The Society also settled disputes between masters and apprentices.

Relations between the Society of Apothecaries and the College of Physicians were good at first, though they deteriorated later because the physicians objected to the apothecaries dispensing medicine without a physician's prescription and the apothecaries objected to physicians dispensing their own medicines. Since the physician's fee was high, normally the gold coin called an angel for each consultation, the poor usually sought medical advice as well as treatment from the apothecary. Nicholas Culpeper, an apothecary and an outspoken critic of the College of Physicians, is reported to have said that physicians were like Balaam's ass – they would only speak when they saw an angel.[11]

A leading apothecary, Gideon Delaune, Master of the Society in 1628–9 and 1637–8, encouraged co-operation with the physicians and did much to promote the prestige of the Society. When the College of Physicians in its centenary year (1618) published by royal command its *Pharmacopoea Londinensis* (Fig 1) the physicians preparing the work had been assisted by the Master, Warden, and three Assistants of the newly created Society of

Figure 1. The *London Pharmacopoeia* (Courtesy of the Royal College of Physicians of London)

Apothecaries.[12] The pharmacopoeia embodied the pharmacy of the time; unfortunately in later editions, until that of 1788, it failed to advance with the times. Contrary to the wishes of the College, an English edition was published in 1649 by Nicholas Culpeper; physicians and most apothecaries preferred that the details of pharmacy should be kept from the general public by being written in Latin. A new edition in Latin was published by the College in 1650 and a third in 1677. A revised edition of Culpeper's translation, with comments, was published in 1683.

From 1633, when the apothecaries were established for the first time in premises of their own, physicians were invited to be present at the examination of those to be made freemen of the Society. The relationship between the two professions was, however, in unstable equilibrium and the balance was upset in 1675, when the College proposed to set up a dispensary for the sick poor, at which the physicians would give free advice and the apothecaries were asked to provide the prescribed medicines cheaply.[13] Although agreement was reached in principle and the dispensary started to function in 1697 a dispute on the details persisted until 1699, when it was brought to an abrupt end by the publication of a satirical poem, *Dispensary*, by Dr Samuel Garth, which ridiculed both groups. The dispensary functioned until 1725.

Throughout the seventeenth century there was intermittent strife between the College and the Society on the right of the apothecary to prescribe as well as to dispense medicine, a conflict won in the next century by the apothecaries. William Rose, an apothecary, was sued by the College of Physicians in 1701 for treating a patient without a physician being involved. He lost the case but the verdict was reversed in 1703 in a decision by the House of Lords that it would be 'against the public interest to prevent the giving of advice and treatment by members of the Apothecaries' Company'.[14]

The surgeon

The Barber-Surgeons' Company, established in 1540 (p. 108) was responsible for the supervision of surgery. Apprentices had to serve seven years and pass an examination before admission to the Company. By a charter of 1629 surgical practice in London, and for seven miles around, was restricted to members of the Company, but the Bishop of London or the Dean of St Paul's sometimes granted licences to surgeons who had not been approved by the Company.[15] The surgeons had to fight for their rights against the College of Physicians, which obtained a charter in 1617 forbidding non-members of the College to administer internal medicines; the surgeons' privileges were restored in their charter of 1629. In 1632 the physicians obtained an Order in Council forbidding major operations except in the presence of a member of the College; this was rescinded in 1635.[16]

In 1638 the Company opened an anatomical theatre and a livery hall for formal meetings. Public demonstrations and lectures in anatomy were given, usually by a Fellow of the College of Physicians. The buildings were destroyed in 1666 by the Great Fire of London and rebuilt shortly afterwards on the same site. Owing to the heavy demands on the guilds by King and Parliament for 'loans' the Company was often in financial difficulties and towards the end of the century there was a shortage of Company's apprentices when would-be surgeons found that they could get better training assisting a surgeon at St Bartholomew's or St Thomas's Hospital than as an apprentice to a member of the Company.

There were surgeons' guilds in other English towns, including Exeter, Norwich, Bristol, York and Newcastle, mostly following the London pattern but with some variations; in York the barber-surgeons were combined with physicians and in Norwich with physicians and apothecaries. Some members in York and in Norwich were women.[17]

At the beginning of the seventeenth century the leading surgeons in England had gained their experience in war. John Woodall (p. 109), who was appointed surgeon to St Bartholomew's Hospital while William Harvey was physician, had been an army surgeon and was the first surgeon-general of the Association of Merchant-Adventurers (East India Company). Richard Wiseman (p. 111), the outstanding surgeon of the century, served in the Royalist army in the First Civil War. Peter Lowe, a Scotsman with extensive experience as an army surgeon in France and Flanders, published *The Whole Course of Chirurgerie* (1597); this and subsequent editions were very influential in the first half of the seventeenth century. Another Scot who contributed to English surgery was Alexander Read, whose *Surgical Operations* was first published in 1672. Joseph Binns (p. 113), a London surgeon, kept a detailed case-book from 1633 to 1663, which has never been published. None of these books show any significant advance on Tudor surgery.

The midwife

Midwifery was no part of orthodox medicine in the seventeenth century. As in earlier times it was usually performed by 'wise women', some of whom might have a certificate of competence from the bishop of the diocese on the recommendation of a local medical practitioner, but the Church was more concerned with the midwife's religious orthodoxy than with her skill. The licensed midwife had to promise to employ no sorcery and to baptise the child if it seemed likely to die before being brought to a priest.[18] In general midwives ranked low in the social scale but a few were gentlewomen. The better class of midwife worked as a deputy for some years to gain experience and might pay for training as well as, later, for a licence.[19]

In the seventeenth century there were a few man-midwives who might be called in to difficult cases or when the midwife had been unable to deliver a dead child. Some physicians performed obstetrics on some of their upper-class patients. William Harvey was highly esteemed as an obstetrician.[20] The Chamberlen family of man-midwives invented the obstetric forceps but managed to keep it secret for about a century (p. 123).

The nurse

Nursing hardly formed part of the pattern of English medicine in the seventeenth century. There was no organised nursing profession and most nursing was performed by the women of the family. Professional nurses usually came from the lowest social classes and were untrained, although those working in the hospitals were of higher status and under some medical supervision. A midwife often functioned also as a nurse.

The housewife

The womenfolk of the family would not only nurse the sick but also treat minor ailments and injuries. Herbal lore was quite widespread, especially among the upper classes, and, in a rural society which retained some elements of feudalism, the lady of the manor might treat and, if necessary, make arrangements for nursing the sick villagers.

Most of the domestic prescriptions which have been preserved from the seventeenth century are in 'receipt books' of the aristocracy, e.g. Lady Hoby, the Countess of Kent, Lady Ranelagh, and Lady Catherine Sedley.[21] Lady Sedley's books include prescriptions by leading physicians (p. 136).

Dr George Wharton, an eminent physician, complained that 'all our ladies and gentlemen keeps and stores up receipt books and closetts of medicines fitted for most occasions'.[22] Dr Gideon Harvey, physician to King Charles II and a thorn in the flesh of the College of Physicians, encouraged domestic treatment in his book, *The Family Physician and the House Apothecary* (1676).

Clergy

The clergy were no part of organised medicine in the seventeenth century as they had been before the Reformation. They were discouraged from practising medicine by the Church and by the medical profession; the College of Physicians would not grant a clergyman a licence to practise medicine.[23] In spite of this some ordained clergymen, notably Richard Napier (p. 69) and John Ward (p. 139), felt it their duty to treat the sick. Others, including Ralph Josselin, treated only himself and his family and rarely consulted a physician.[24]

The quack

The quack (an abbreviation for quacksalver), is defined in the Shorter Oxford English Dictionary (SOED) as 'an ignorant pretender to medical skill; one who boasts to have a knowledge of wonderful remedies; an empiric or imposter in medicine 1659'. Although this definition does not exclude all duly qualified practitioners it is used more frequently than the term, 'empiric', for 'one who practises physic or surgery without scientific knowledge' (SOED). An empiric's prescription were based on experience and he or she did not advertise. Many housewives and some clergymen were empirics.

Quacks abounded in the seventeenth century, especially during the Civil Wars, when the College of Physicians was unable to exercise even its normal control over unqualified practitioners in London, and during epidemics of plague, when many physicians as well as their wealthy patients left the city.

Many seventeenth-century quacks were mountebanks, a mountebank being an 'itinerant quack who from a platform appealed to his audience by means of stories, tricks, juggling and the like, often with the assistance of a professional clown' (SOED). Some quacks, however, were members of the aristocracy or employed by the king and so, for practical purposes, exempt from prosecution, although their practice was illegal.[25] The best known of these, Sir Kenelm Digby (p. 141) was a privateer in his youth and then a popular writer on pseudo-science. Of humbler origin, Valentine Greatrakes (p. 143) was protected by King Charles II.

At the Restoration many quacks came to England from Germany, Italy, France, and the Low Countries.[26] A famous one, Cornelius Tilburg (p. 143), practised both medicine and surgery. Many quacks practised astrology as well as medicine.

Since no official remedy was effective against plague, unofficial remedies proliferated during epidemics and secret nostrums were advertised. A French quack in London, with the approval of the Privy Council, sold a fumigant against the plague, 'Angier's fume', later found to consist of sulphur, saltpetre, and amber.[27]

Hospitals

In the seventeenth century London was very badly off for hospitals. Only St Bartholomew's, St Thomas's, and Bethlehem (Bedlam) survived Henry VIII's dissolution of the monasteries and no new hospitals were built in London until the eighteenth century, although two buildings, the Savoy and Ely House, were requisitioned as military hospitals in 1642 during the First Civil War and in 1652 for the First Dutch War.[28] Both were closed at the Restoration. From early in the fifteenth century Bedlam was a hospital for the insane; it was run by a keeper for his private profit until 1663, when the Bridewell governors, who were also governors of Bedlam, appointed a steward responsible to them.[29] Although the patients often suffered neglect and even starvation, they were not otherwise ill-used at that time.

Hospitals were homes for the aged poor as much as centres for medical care. They accommodated only a very small proportion of the sick. Nursing was primitive but under some control by the physician in charge. London was more poorly provided with isolation hospitals outside the city than were many cities on the continent of Europe. The city of London had one small isolation hospital at St Giles-without-Cripplegate and Westminster had one in Tothill Fields.[30] During epidemics of plague these were totally inadequate.

CHAPTER 2

Brief Lives of Some Physicians

IN THE SEVENTEENTH CENTURY a physician's training was so expensive that only a wealthy family could afford it. The profession did not attract the nobility, who were concerned with administering their estates, but rather the sons of wealthy land-owners or of merchants. Few physicians were the sons of physicians.[1] The would-be physician had to be at least a competent classical scholar but the most successful were not necessarily the most highly qualified. Then, as now, the 'bedside manner' must have contributed greatly to the success of the leading members of the profession. During the Civil Wars and the Interregnum political considerations were also important and overt support of the Royalist or Parliamentary cause could make or mar a promising career.

A brief biography of some of the outstanding figures and a couple of the less well-known in seventeenth-century English medicine illustrates the background to their practice and some of their other contributions to society. In this chapter they are divided arbitrarily into medical scientists, whose main contribution to the future of medicine was a better understanding of the structure and function of the human body, and medical practitioners, whose principal contribution was the diagnosis and treatment of disease. The division is artibrary because all the medical scientists described in this chapter were also successful practitioners of medicine. Another arbitrary division is between London and country practitioners; the latter were thrown more on their own resources and had less ready access to a 'second opinion' but they were by no means out of touch with their metropolitan colleagues and they practised the same sort of medicine.

In seventeenth-century Europe there were two distinctly different modes of medical treatment. The traditional 'galenists' prescribed herbal remedies (p. 39), whereas the 'paracelsians', following the lead of Paracelsus (p. 44), preferred inorganic remedies; the paracelsians were also called iatrochemists. Most English physicians were prepared to use plant material or inorganic remedies in the light of their own experience of what had proved effective but some were strong protagonists of one or other school. Among the physicians described in this chapter Baldwin Hamey is selected as an example of a galenist and Edmund Dickinson was a paracelsian.

Medical Scientists

William Harvey

William Harvey (Fig 2), generally considered to be the leading medical scientist of the century, was born in Folkestone in 1578, the eldest son of the second marriage of Thomas Harvey, a prosperous merchant, who later became mayor of Folkestone. William had 6 brothers, 3 of whom became wealthy merchants, and 2 sisters, one of whom died in childhood. At the age of 26 he married Elizabeth, daughter of Dr Lancelot Browne, physician to the king. Little is known about their married life except that they had no children. Elizabeth died about ten years before William, who died in 1657. According to the biographer, John Aubrey: 'He was not tall, but of the lowest stature, round faced, olivaster complexion, little eyes, round, very black, full of spirit, his hair was black as a raven but quite white twenty years before he died.'[2]

Harvey was educated at King's School, Canterbury, which he entered in 1588, the year of the Spanish Armada, and thereafter at Gonville and Caius College, Cambridge, where he graduated as Bachelor of Arts in 1597. In 1598 he went to Padua to study medicine. His teacher of anatomy there was Fabricius of Aquapendente, an Aristotelian whose influence on Harvey appears in the numerous references to Aristotle's zoological observations in Harvey's anatomical lectures. In 1602 Harvey graduated as Doctor of Medicine at Padua. His diploma states that 'he had conducted himself so wonderfully well in the examination and had shown such skill, memory and learning that he had far surpassed even the great hopes which his examiners had formed of him.[3] In the same year he was incorporated as a Doctor of Medicine at the University of Cambridge and in 1604 he was admitted as a Candidate of the College of Physicians, of which he became a Fellow in 1607.

Harvey's work as a medical scientist is described in Chapter 5. His professional life as a physician was largely associated with St Bartholomew's Hospital, the College of Physicians, and the royal court as physician to James I and Charles I. In 1609, when he was appointed physician to St

Bartholomew's Hospital, he was the only physician on the staff, which included three surgeons and an apothecary. Harvey's duties were detailed in the 'charge' administered to the newly appointed physician. He was to attend the hospital at least once a week, examine the patients brought to him, and prescribe treatment. The charge states:

Figure 2. William Harvey (Courtesy of the Royal College of Physicians of London)

You shall not for favour, lucre, or gaine appoynte or write anything for the poore but such good and wholesome things as you shall thinke with your best advise will do the poore good . . . and you shall take no gifte or reward of any of the poore of this house for your counsell.[4]

While he was physician to the hospital Havey proved a competent administrator, presenting to the governors a number of orders for the better organisation of the hospital, all of which were approved and some of which are still observed. In his regulations Harvey was at pains to maintain the superior status of the physician over the surgeons. It was decreed

that the Chirurgions, in all difficult cases or where inward physic may be necessary, shall consult the Doctor, at the times he sitteth once in the week and then . . . relate to the Doctor what he conceiveth of the cure and what he hath done therein. And in a decent and orderly manner proceed by the Doctor's directions for the good of the poor and credit of the house.[5]

By the time Harvey was appointed physician extraordinary to King James I in 1618 he was already physician to many of the most distinguished people in London and a popular consultant. Unfortunately only one of his reports has been preserved, a letter to Dr Baldwin Hamey (p. 20). With spelling and punctuation modernised it reads as follows:

Most learned, humane and dear Sir,

The woman appears to me, from her own account, and her mode of life (with deference to your judgement) to be affected with a cholic passion of a hot and bilious nature. Suppose it was pitchy stuff that was formally discharged [black stools?], still I do not believe that there is any imposthume [abscess] in the hypochondriac or epigastric region; I should else have detected either some enlargement or some tenderness there. I therefore approve of your decision as to blood-letting; for the plethoric body of the patient, accustomed to generous diet, hot, robust, and vigorous, requires it. I also recommend purging by the Cholagogue Pills, with half a scruple of Euphorbia added, this medicine having an excellent effect in soothing colic pains. I also advise the frequent use of the powder of ivory and *calcaneum cervi*. Everything else I leave to your discretion

Farewell, my very dear Sir,
Yours with all my heart,
Will Harvey[6]

From such of his prescriptions as have been preserved it is evident that Harvey's medical practice was orthodox, though his treatment was simpler than that of most other physicians. When he attended Prince Maurice in 1643 he prescribed 'very little phisick' and 'only a regular dyett and Cordyall Antidotes.'[7] His reluctance to prescribe drugs unless there seemed to be some need for them was ridiculed by some of his contemporaries and Aubrey relates: 'I knew several practisers in London towne that would not have given threepence for one of his bills [prescriptions].[8]

When the First Civil War started in 1642 Harvey left London with the king and he spent the next four years with the royal court at Oxford. As a royalist he was *persona non grata* in London, where the House of Commons resolved that he should be dismissed from his hospital appointment. In 1642 he was incorporated as a Doctor of Medicine of Oxford and in 1645 was appointed warden of Merton College. Apart from some minor reorganisation he had little time to do anything for the College because the post reverted to a parliamentary supporter the following year, when Oxford fell to the king's enemies and Harvey returned to London. He took little part in public life thereafter, except for the affairs of the College of Physicians, in which he continued to take an active interest for the rest of his life.

Harvey's work as a medical scientist was performed largely under the auspices of the College of Physicians and he took an active part in its administration. He was a censor of the College and treasurer but never president. His firm adherence to the royalist cause would have made it difficult for the College to appoint him to this office during or shortly after the Civil Wars but his prestige as a scientist helped the predominantly royalist College to survive the defeat of the royalists. When unanimously chosen as president in 1654 he declined the honour on the grounds of age and infirmity.

During his retirement Harvey turned his still active mind to the study of general literature, writing to a friend:

'I myself, though verging on my eightieth year and sorely failed in bodily health, nevertheless feel my mind still vigorous, so that I continue to give myself to studies of this kind, especially connected with the sacred things of Apollo'[9]

According to Dr Charles Scarburgh, his successor in the Lumleian lectureship, 'the sharpness of his intellect continued unimpaired and a certain youthful disposition persisted to the end.'[10]

Francis Glisson

Francis Glisson wrote important works on the anatomy of the liver (p. 77) and the physiology of muscle (p. 86) but was also an eminent London physician. Less is known about his family life than that of some other eminent physicians but Munk records that he was born in 1597 at Rampisham in Dorsetshire, the second son of William Glisson.[11] His medical education was at Caius College, Cambridge, although he incorporated one of his degrees at Oxford. He graduated BA in 1621, MA in 1624, and MD in 1634, in which year he was admitted a Candidate of the College of Physicians. In 1635 he was admitted a Fellow of the College and in 1636 he was appointed Regius Professor of Physic at Cambridge, a post which he held until his death in 1677, although shortly after the Civil Wars he moved his residence to London. A man of many parts, Glisson was a founder member of the Royal Society in 1662 and president of the College of Physicians from 1667 to 1669.

Glisson's greatest contribution to clinical medicine was his epoch-making book on rickets, *De rachitide seu morbo puerili* (1650). Although the original plan was for three physicians, Drs Glisson, Bate and Regemorter, to write the book, so much was written by Glisson that the other two invited him to publish it as the sole author, although 'they would assist him still with their advice and judgment and contribute their own observations'.[12] An English translation by P. Armin was published the following year as *A treatise of the Rickets*. Rickets is described as a new disease; although it had probably been endemic in England for centuries it first appeared in the London Bills of Mortality in 1634. Another London physician, Daniel Whistler, had written in 1645 a treatise on the disease, *De morbo puerili anglorum quem patrio idiomate indigenae vocant The Rickets*, but Glisson's description of the disease corresponds more closely to what we recognise today. The chest is shaped 'like the breast of a hen and the ribs are swollen where they join the breastbone'.[13] Other features he noted are a protuberant abdomen, deformities of the limbs, especially of weight-bearing bones, and sometimes gross deformity of the spine. Glisson noted that rickets is a disease of childhood but does not usually appear until the child is at least 9 months old. It was commoner in the children of the rich; these children would not usually be suckled by their mothers as poor children were. James I probably had rickets and Charles I certainly had it.[14] Rickets was known on the continent of Europe as the English disease and Glisson suggested that its prevalence in England might be due to the climate. No further explanation of the cause of the disease was offered and no effective treatment was known, though the use of splints was recommended to limit deformities of the limbs and spine.[15]

The cause and treatment of rickets were discovered only in 1919 by Edward Mellanby, the cause being lack of vitamin D, present in animal fats and formed in the skin when exposed to sunshine, and the treatment provision of this vitamin, conveniently in cod liver oil, which is rich in it. Glisson's observations on the incidence of the disease can be accounted for by the lack of milk fat in the diet of rich children, briefly suckled by a wet nurse and weaned early on to a diet poor in animal fat and by the lack of sunshine in the English climate.

Thomas Willis

More is known about the life of another distinguished medical scientist, Thomas Willis, who was born in 1621 at Great Bedwin in Wiltshire, the son of a prosperous farmer. He was educated at a private school in Oxford, entered Christ Church College in 1636, and graduated BA in 1639 and MA in 1642. 'About that time', according to Munk, 'he bore arms for the king'.[16] He then devoted himself to the study of medicine and took his degree of Bachelor of Medicine in 1646. He practised medicine at Oxford, where in 1660, shortly after the Restoration, he was appointed professor of natural philosophy and created Doctor of Medicine. He lectured on medical topics instead of, as was expected of him, on Aristotle and he conducted anatomical dissections.[17] An incident in connection with one of these attracted more than merely professional attention. He detected signs of life in the body of Ann Green, a servant girl hanged for infanticide and sent to him for dissection; with the aid of one of his colleagues, William Petty (p. 89), he revived her and she was allowed to go free.[18]

In the words of a contemporary:

'He was a plain Man, a Man of no Carriage, little Discourse, Complaisance or Society, yet for his deep Insight, happy Researches in natural and experimental Philosophy, Anatomy, and Chymistry, for his wonderful Success and Repute in his practice, the natural smoothness, pure elegancy, delightful unaffected neatness of Latin style, none scarce have equalled, much less outshone him how great soever.'[19]

He was a strong supporter of the Anglican church and, from 1646 while the Puritans were in power, he had services held in his house according to the rites of the Church of England. In 1657 he married Mary Fell, daughter of one vice-Chancellor of Oxford University and sister of his successor, Dr John Fell, who had conducted Anglican worship in Willis's home during the Interregnum.

At Oxford Willis was active in scientific research (Chapter 5) as well as medical practice. He was one of the original members of the Royal Society and in 1664 became an Honorary Fellow of the College of Physicians. In 1667, the year he moved to London, his income (£300 a year) was reputed to be the highest in Oxford.[20] He was a conscientious and observant practitioner and his Oxford case-book, the only one which has been preserved, reveals that his practice was transitional between galenism and paracelcism; he employed herbal or chemical remedies, whichever seemed more appropriate or both.

Willis's *Two Discourses Concerning the Soul of Brutes* (1672), translated into English in 1683, contained the best descriptions of nervous diseases to date; these included headache, lethargy, vertigo, apoplexy, palsy, delirium, melancholy, and madness. He was also the first to describe and name puerperal fever and, from his military experience, he gave the first account of epidemic typhus fever (p. 163) as it occurred in the troops during the First Civil War.[21] He also described an epidemic of what was probably influenza in 1658.[22] His *Pharmaceutica rationalis* (1679), published a year before his death, included an excellent description of diabetes mellitus, which he regarded as a disease of the blood and not of the kidneys, as was supposed at the time.[23] The primary cause of the disease is lack of a hormone, insulin, produced in the pancreas and first discovered in 1922 by two Canadians, a surgeon, Frederick Banting, and a medical student, Charles Best.

Willis was the foremost and probably the safest physician of his day.[24] Although he had a busy aristocratic practice in London he offended some patients by his lack of tact. According to Munk:

Dr Willis, if not the regular physician to the Duke of York, afterwards James II, or to some members of his family, was certainly consulted on the state of health of the male children of that prince by his first wife, all of whom were, it seems, suffering more or less from disease originating in the amours of their father [syphilis]. Dr Willis spoke his mind freely, but by doing so gave great offence, and was never afterwards consulted.[25]

London Physicians

Sir Theodore de Mayerne

Theodore de Mayerne was one of the numerous French Protestants who sought refuge in England during the seventeenth century. He became a royal physician and made important contributions to English medicine.

Theodore, the son of a distinguished French historian, was born in Geneva in 1573. He spent some years at the University of Heidelberg and then studied medicine at Montpellier, where he graduated Bachelor of Medicine in 1596 and Doctor of Medicine in 1597. He then moved to Paris, where he practised medicine and lectured on anatomy to surgeons and on pharmacy to apothecaries. His recommendation and use of chemical remedies roused the wrath of the very conservative Faculty of Medicine of Paris but his appointment as a physician in ordinary to King Henry IV gave him some immunity.[26] In 1606 he incorporated his degree at Oxford and was appointed by King James I of England as physician to his queen, Anne of Denmark. He was back in France in 1610 when Henry was assassinated but then returned to England at the request of King James to be first physician to himself and his queen. Little is known about de Mayerne's family life except that he was married more than once and had more than five children.[27]

In 1616 de Mayerne was elected a Fellow of the College of Physicians. In 1617 his active support helped his fellow-countryman, Gideon Delaune, and others to found the Society of Apothecaries[28] and he wrote much of the first edition of the *Pharmacopoea Londinensis*, which was published in 1618. Munk credits him with the introduction of calomel (mercurous chloride) and black wash (calomel and glycerine in lime water) into medical practice. Although he published very little under his own name, he was in great demand as a consultant and his case-book from 1634 to 1649 reveals that his practice was very aristocratic, including English and French nobility.[29] The conditions he treated ranged from 'redness of the face' to phthisis and he prescribed cosmetics for two queens of England, Anne of Denmark and Henrietta Maria.

Some of de Mayerne's letters, originally written in French and later translated into Latin, were translated into English and edited by T. Shirley in 1677. Advice given in 1645 to a French nobleman suffering from consumption (pulmonary tuberculosis) shows that Mayerne was prepared to prescribe animal and herbal remedies, as he considered appropriate. Tobacco is useful but wine should be avoided. A useful syrup is 'made with the flesh of *Tortoise, Snails,* the *Lungs* of *Animals, Froggs* and *Craw-fish,* all boyl'd in *Scabiose* and *Colts-foot water,* adding at last *Sugar Candy'*.[30] In other letters he offered advice for the prevention and cure of plague during the major epidemic of 1625 (Chapter 10).

De Mayerne was knighted in 1624 and, on the accession of Charles I to the throne the following year, was appointed First Physician to the new king and queen. There is no record of his taking any part in the Civil Wars and he died in 1655, leaving his large library to the College of Physicians.

Baldwin Hamey

Baldwin Hamey was the son of a Huguenot refugee physician of the same name. His father was a native of Bruges who studied medicine at Leyden before moving to London, where he practised medicine for forty-two years as a Licentiate of the College of Physicians.[31] Baldwin Jnr was born in London in 1590 and attended one of the city schools. He then studied, like his father, at the University of Leyden, where he graduated MD in 1626. After further study at the universities of Paris, Montpellier, and Padua he incorporated his Leyden degree at Oxford and started to practise medicine in London.

> As to his person he was but of low stature yet of a comely mien and his aspect engaging. He had full beautifull and black eyes wherein sat majesty and gracefulness in conjunct dominion, his hair was black which he always wore nor long nor short but not curling. He had a well turned face and a very graceful elevation in the carriage of his head easy and free too without stiffness or affection and every feature of his countenance was good.[32]

Hamey married a Dutch girl and the marriage was happy though childless. On his incorporation at Oxford Hamey became a Candidate of the

College of Physicians. He became a Fellow in 1644 and thereafter held many official posts in the College, including the Lectureship in Anatomy in 1647.

> As a faithful member of the Church of England, and a devoted royalist, he was dismayed by the political events which marked the early years of his practice, and at one time, though then getting into full professional employment, had serious thoughts of quitting London.[33]

Nevertheless he remained and developed a large and wealthy practice. This included some leading Puritans, who introduced the symptoms of their venereal disease with 'a long religious preface' or described them as the symptoms of some near relative or friend.

Although his practice included leading figures of the Commonwealth Hamey's sympathies were entirely with the royal family and he sent several sums of money to Charles II during his exile. At the Restoration, anticipating his retirement, he declined a knighthood and the post of first physician to the king. Being wealthy and childless the 'not parsimonious' Hamey was a 'munificent benefactor' of the College of Physicians and of the Church and when he died in 1676 he left most of his estate to the College.

In his practice Hamey was a convinced galenist, suspicious of science and jealous of the Royal Society.[34] He published nothing but his dissertation on quinsy for his Leyden degree and he left an unfinished manuscript on Hippocrates but his many notes and observations, often written in the volumes of his large library, show him to have been a traditional physician.

Edmund Dickinson

In contrast to Baldwin Hamey, Edmund Dickinson is remembered mainly for his faith in chemical (paracelsian) remedies. He was born in 1624, the son of a Berkshire rector, and educated at Eton and Merton College, Oxford, where he graduated BA in 1647 and MA in 1649. Although he was a brilliant classical scholar, and encouraged by his teachers and the Archbishop of Canterbury to become a clergyman, he decided to study medicine and graduated Doctor of medicine in 1656. In the previous year he had published a very learned work, *Delphi Phaenicizantes,* in which he traced Greek religious practices from Hebrew origins.[35]

As to his Person, he was of middle Stature, yet had a good Presence, which being assisted by a lively Eye, commanded Respect; sober and temperate in his Diet; of an open and generous Disposition, which made him easily shake off the narrow Spirit and Moroseness generally contracted by those who have led a College Life.[36]

After his graduation in medicine Dickinson studied chemistry and, according to Munk, 'eventually became the highest authority on that subject in this country'.[37] In 1662 he took a house in Oxford 'and practised [medicine] with great Credit and Success'. His first wife died after giving birth to his only child, a daughter, after which he moved to London and married again, his second wife dying without issue. Thereafter he remained a widower, practising medicine in London.

Like other extreme paracelsians, Dickinson believed that mercury and sulphur are the two essential drugs for the treatment of disease.[38] Unlike the others, however, he rejected astrology as a false science. Since almost all his published work was on theology little is known of his medical practice except that it was successful. He was elected to Fellowship of the College of Physicians in 1667 and was Physician in Ordinary to King Charles II and King James II. He retired from medical practice in 1688, when James II was deposed, and devoted his time to philosophy until his death in 1707.

Thomas Sydenham

Just as William Harvey is generally regarded as the leading medical scientist of the seventeenth century, Thomas Sydenham is considered to be the leading medical practitioner of the period. According to his latest biographer: 'the sound judgment and acute observations of Thomas Sydenham, the English Hippocrates, freed clinical medicine from the last vestiges of medievalism and set the pattern for further progress'.[39] The term, English Hippocrates, is appropriate because Sydenham relied for diagnosis on a full history and careful examination of the patient instead of on astrology or uroscopy (p. 47), which were often regarded at the time as adequate substitutes for this. He also kept meticulous records of his patients' physical signs and symptoms and of his treatment and its effects. He did not, however, 'free medicine from the last vestiges of medievalism' because much of his treatment was based, as in the Middle Ages, on the precepts of Galen. In one respect 'he set the pattern for further progress' by attempting to identify and classify particular diseases, as his contemporaries in the Royal Society were identifying and classifying plants, animals, and minerals. In another respect, however, he hindered progress by ignoring the important advances in medical science being made by his contemporaries which, more than Sydenham's work, paved the way for scientific medicine.

Thomas Sydenham (Fig. 3) was born at Wynford Eagle in Dorset in 1624, the fifth son of a country gentleman. His father, William, had seven

Figure 3. Thomas Sydenham (Courtesy of the Royal College of Physicians of London)

sons and three daughters. Two of the sons died young, four (including Thomas) served in the Parliamentary army in the Civil Wars, and the other was a civil commissioner under the Commonwealth and Protectorate. The eldest son, William, became a colonel, two were killed in action, and Thomas was wounded twice. The daughters reached adulthood and married.

In 1642 Thomas matriculated at Magdalen Hall, at that time a centre of Oxford Puritanism, but after a few months he left to join the Parliamentary army as a cornet of horse. In 1646, after the First Civil War, he returned to Oxford and in 1648 he became a Bachelor of Medicine by 'actual creation', a scheme adopted in these troubled times whereby a degree could be granted without the preparation and examination usually required. 'He had thus the rare good fortune to obtain a degree at the beginning instead of at the end of his student's course.'[40] He was then appointed to a Fellowship of All Souls' College, probably in place of a displaced Royalist.

In 1651 Sydenham rejoined Cromwell's army, this time as a captain of cavalry, for the war in Scotland. After six months and his second wound he returned to Oxford to resume his Fellowship and his studies. In 1655 he married Mary Gee at Wynford Eagle and, as required by university statutes, resigned his Fellowship on marriage. Soon afterwards he bought a house in Westminster and began to practise there as a physician. After at least three years of unlicensed medical practice he passed the examination to become a Licentiate of the College of Physicians and moved to Pall Mall, where he spent the remainder of his life, except during the Great Plague, when he fled the city. He was on good terms with the College of Physicians, though he never became a Fellow. By 1676, when he became a Doctor of Medicine (of Cambridge) and was therefore eligible for the Fellowship, he was already the leading physician in the city and presumably did not covet any further distinctions.

Little is known of Sydenham's home life. He had three sons, the eldest of whom joined him in medical practice, and his wife predeceased him. He suffered from gout and from stone in the bladder, which sometimes incapacitated him for long periods. He died in 1689.

At Oxford Sydenham was a close friend of Robert Boyle and John Locke. It is odd that he was not stimulated to an interest in experimental science by Boyle, to whom he dedicated his first major work, or to an interest in philosophy by Locke, who was his apprentice for a time in medical practice and recorded some of his observations. Other Oxford contemporaries were Christopher Wren and Robert Hooke, both of them scientists and architects, William Petty, physician, economist, and statistician, and Thomas Millington, who later became president of the College of Physicians. It was a distinguished company. Among those who later learnt clinical medicine by working with Sydenham were Richard Blackmore, who became a very wealthy and fashionable physician, Thomas Dover, buccaneer and physician, Hans Sloane, later president of the College of Physicians and of the Royal Society and virtual founder of the British Museum, and Charles Goodall, another future president of the College of Physicians.

Sydenham had an essentially practical attitude to medicine, which he believed should be learnt at the bedside rather than from books. Although he derived his theories of disease from the works of Hippocrates and Galen and he would not have written books on medicine if he had not expected people to read them, he constantly stressed the need for careful detailed observation of the sick as the basis of medical practice. This empirical approach may be attributed to Sydenham's early training. He was a soldier rather than a scholar and never completed the course of classical studies then required of a medical student. His only academic experience was at Oxford University, where theoretical teaching in medicine was poor and there was little dissection and no clinical instruction.

Sydenham accepted the traditional galenic doctrine of the four humours, blood, phlegm, yellow bile and black bile (p. 36), and his treatment was usually designed to correct the imbalance of these which was assumed to be the cause of the illness. He believed, however, that disease could also be due to inhalation of tainted particles or to putrefaction of humours in the body.[41] The symptoms represented a vigorous attempt by Nature to throw off the 'morbific matter' and permit recovery. The physician's duty was to assist Nature to do this.

Sydenham believed that knowledge of the anatomy of spleen, liver, or kidney is no guide to understanding their function. Writing fifty-five years after the publication of Harvey's *De motu cordis* he ignored the new knowledge of the circulation of the blood, and more than twenty years after Marcello Malpighi had reported his discovery of the capillaries Sydenham wrote: 'No microscope will ever show us the minute passages by which the chyle leaves the intestine, or show by which the blood passes

THOMÆ SYDENHAM
METHODUS
CURANDI FEBRES,
Propriis Observationibus Superstructa.

Multa egerunt qui ante nos fuerunt, sed non peregerunt : multum adhuc restat operæ, multumq; restabit : neq; ulli nato post mille sæcula præcidetur occasio aliquid adhuc adjiciendi. Seneca.

LONDINI,

Impensis *J. Crook*, apud quem veneunt sub Signo *Navis* in Cœmeterio D. *Pauli*. MDCLXVI.

Figure 4. Title page of *Methodus curandi febres* by Thomas Syndeham (Courtesy of the Royal Society of Medicine)

from the arteries to the veins'.[42] He also affirmed that the human intellect would never be able to understand the function of the different parts of the brain, some aspects of which his contemporary, Thomas Willis, had already discovered and described (p. 77).

With the possible exception of his first major work, *Methodus curandi febres* (Fig. 4) Sydenham wrote in English but, to make his works 'respectable' for publication, they were translated into Latin by his friends, especially Gilbert Havers, a classical scholar, and John Mapletoft, a physician.[43] They have been translated back into English by J. Pechey (1696), J. Swan (1743), R. G. Latham (1848), and J. D. Comrie (1922). Pechey's own *Collections of Acute Diseases* (1691) is mainly a summary of Sydenham's ideas.

In *Methodus curandi febres* (1666) Sydenham classified fevers as continual (including what would now be identified as typhoid and typhus), intermittent (including malaria) and smallpox. A second edition, in 1668, included a chapter on plague, of which Sydenham had little practical experience (p. 24), and in 1676 an enlarged edition was published under the title of *Observationes medicae*. In this book Sydenham described the epidemic diseases in London from 1661 to 1675. He believed that each period of two or three years was characterised by a particular 'epidemic constitution' or disposition of the atmosphere in which a particular fever or group of fevers predominates.[44] This is a Hippocratic concept (p. 38).

In a separate short paper on scarlet fever Sydenham wrote that it was commonest in children in late summer and was of little consequence.

> I reckon this Disease is nothing else but a moderate effervescence of the Blood, occasion'd by the Heat of the foregoing Summer, or some other way, and therefore I do nothing to hinder Despumation [removal of froth] of the Blood and the ejecting of the peccant Matter thro the Pores of the Skin . . . I think it sufficient that the Sick abstain wholly from Flesh and from all spirituous Liquors whatever, and that he keep always within but not always a-bed.[45]

After *Methodus curandi febres* which became *Observationes medicae*, Sydenham's best-known book is *Tractatus de podagra et hydrope* (1683), a treatise on gout and oedema. Himself a sufferer from gout, Sydenham writes: 'it may be some consolation to the sufferers from the disease, who like myself and others are only moderately endowed with fortune and intellectual gifts, that great kings, princes, generals, philosophers and many of like eminence have suffered from the same complaint.'[46] Sydenham noted that eating and drinking to excess and lack of exercise would bring on an attack in those susceptible to the disease. He described the symptoms (p. 55) in some detail.

The same treatise deals with dropsy. Though dropsy (oedema) is now recognised as a complication of several quite different disorders, Sydenham considered it a specific disease. He noted accumulation of fluid first in the lower part of the legs, then higher and in the thighs and, in severe cases, in the abdomen, where it could hinder the descent of the diaphragm and cause difficulty in breathing. Although the cause of the condition was obscure the obvious treatment was to get rid of the fluid. Sydenham attempted to do this with purgatives, of which the following is an example: 'Take of the Water of *Carduus Benedictus* three Ounces; of the Infusion of *Crocus Metallorum* one Ounce and a half; of the Electuary of the Juice of Roses two Drams; mingle them, make a potion'.[47]

Some other publications by Sydenham were in the form of long letters in reply to questions from medical colleagues. His first such 'epistolary discourse' was to Dr Brady, Professor of Physick at Cambridge, on 'Epidemical Diseases from the year 1675 to the year 1680'; this brought up to date his previous record from 1661 to 1675. Other letters were on 'The History and Cure of the French Pox' (syphilis), and on 'Confluent Small-Pox and Hysterick Diseases'. Sydenham also wrote to his friend, Dr Charles Goodall, a future president of the College of Physicians, about 'a new fever', which broke out in 1685, with cough, headache, difficulty in breathing, and often pains in the limbs.[48] In children there might be the involuntary movements of limbs (St Vitus's dance), now called Sydenham's chorea, which we associate with rheumatic fever (p. 56).

Sydenham's last publication was an autobiographical essay, *Of a Bloody Urine from a Stone in the Kidney* (1686), ending with the words: 'and this is in a manner the Sum of all which I have hitherto known concerning the Cure of Diseases, *viz*, to the 29th of September 1686.'[49] Some other essays were published posthumously and some are available only in manuscript. Most are on medical topics, expanding on some part of his published work, but one, *Theologia rationalis*, is an expression of the Puritan faith in which he was brought up, his *Religio medici*.

Country Physicians

Less is known about provincial physicians than about those who practised in London because of their relative isolation and because few of them wrote books. Each of the ones we know about lived in a town but every town in England except London was small so most of the practice would be in the surrounding countryside and it is reasonable to call them country physicians.

John Symcotts

The life and work of one country physician, John Symcotts, has been studied and described by Poynter and Bishop from manuscripts, including a case-book, receipt book, letters, and other documents passed down through branches of the family.

John Symcotts was born about 1592, the son of a country gentleman of the same name in Huntingdon. He had three brothers, two of whom had sons who became doctors, but John, though married, had no children. He entered Queen's College, Cambridge, in 1608 and graduated BA in 1612, MA in 1615, and MD from King's College in 1636. He was practising medicine in Huntingdonshire and Bedfordshire for some years before he became a Doctor of Medicine and he had an assistant, Gervase Fulwood, who probably held a bishop's licence to practise but had no university degree.[50] Like the more famous Sydenham, Symcotts came from a Puritan family and actively supported the parliamentary cause in the Civil Wars, thereafter serving on Commonwealth and Protectorate commissions for the county of Huntingdon. He included Oliver Cromwell and family in his practice, which included rich and poor, from the nobility through wealthy merchants to humbler folk. Normally he would visit, on horseback, only patients of high social status; others would come to him or receive instructions by letter. Even the wealthy might not think it necessary to see the doctor personally; the Bishop of Lincoln sent a sample of urine and a letter describing his symptoms and asking for advice.[51] Gervase Fulwood made up the medicines, sent the bills, and acted as *locum tenens* in Symcotts's absence; he had a 'man', Edward Johnson, who assisted in preparing and delivering medicines.

Symcotts's brother, Thomas, commented on his 'lean and spare body'. 'In early life the doctor suffered from headaches, which he eventually cured with a diet drink. On his own statement he had three attacks of smallpox, and he was, during the last years of his life, a martyr to gout.'[52]

Diseases common in the practice were gout, urinary stone, asthma, consumption, agues, pleurisy, smallpox, epilepsy, and (in children) worm infestation. Others mentioned include hernia, gallstones, and haemorrhoids. Symcotts's treatment was the conventional blood-letting, purging, and emetics with (mainly galenical) drugs. Some of his prescriptions were derived from contemporary London physicians and some from 'ladies of quality' or from Gerard's Herbal. In his case-book he describes the course of some illnesses he has observed. Of consumption,

> those that have a long, dry cough, wax lean and thin, feel unequal heats, especially after meals, have a quick small pulse, covet the fire much yet are hot within, and being from the fire grow cold in hands and feet, look pale, are continually troubled with a hoarseness, I never saw recovered.[53]

Again, 'asthmatical coming by fits so vehement that for want of breath the face is red, the shoulders heaved, the pulse quick, all things else being well with them I never saw cured.'[54] Successful cases included a woman with excessive menstrual bleeding, treated with an enema of milk and sugar, a julep of spearmint and watermint with sugar, and an electuary of conserve of roses. Another patient's headache was relieved by applying leeches. A boy, 11 or 12 years old, was cured of fits by purgation, which expelled three large worms. A 'gaping navel' in a one-year-old boy was cured by applying to it a preparation of parsley, knotgrass, and plantain, stamped and made into a plaster with butter.

Letters from Symcotts to Richard Powers, an elderly and difficult patient suffering from gout and other disabilities, are an interesting revelation of the doctor-patient relationship and of the fees charged (for fourteen items ten shillings and nine pence; for sixteen items sixteen shillings and two pence).[55] Although Powers criticised Symcotts's treatment and disputed his bills, Symcotts's letters were consistently courteous and helpful. Fulwood was more abrupt and another employee, Edward Johnson, wrote on one occasion: 'You need not wonder that your cure is no further on foot, you may rather wonder that you was not in your grave long before this.'[56] Correspondence by Symcotts with other medical practitioners and with patients show that he was on good terms with most of his colleagues and that he was willing to receive advice from patients as well as to give it. One titled lady gave him directions for making a 'spleen plaster' and another an ointment for 'fourteen several infirmities'.[57]

In the words of his biographers:

According to the standards of his time Symcotts was a skilled and experienced physician, shrewd, patient, humane, and resourceful. His solicitude for his patients is apparent in every line of his letters and case-books. In his professional ethics he lived up to the high standards of the medical profession.[58]

Symcotts died in 1662.

Sir Thomas Browne

Perhaps the best known physician of the seventeenth century, Sir Thomas Browne, is renowned not for his medical practice but for his writing on religion, philosophy, natural history, and archaeology. His personal faith was expressed in his first and most famous book, *Religio medici* (1642).

Thomas Browne was born in Cheapside, London, in 1605, the only son of a prosperous merchant of the same name, who also had three daughters. It was a deeply religious family, though not bigoted in the sense of extreme adherence to the Anglican, Puritan, or Roman faith. His father died when Thomas was 8 years old and his mother married again. Her second husband, Sir Thomas Dutton 'treated his stepson reasonably well'.[59]

From Munk's Roll we learn that 'his complexion and hair were like his name, brown, his stature moderate, his habit of body neither fat nor lean'. In his clothing 'he had an aversion to all finery'. Of his personality, 'he was never seen to be transported with mirth or dejected with sadness'. Of his learning, 'he understood most of the European languages, Latin and Greek critically, and a little Hebrew'.[60]

Thomas was educated at Winchester College and at Broadgate Hall (now Pembroke College), Oxford, where he graduated BA in 1627. He then studied medicine at Montpellier, Padua, and Leyden, graduating Doctor of Medicine at Leyden about 1633. He practised medicine near Halifax in Yorkshire until 1636, when he moved to Norwich, where he carried on a busy medical practice for the rest of his life. In 1637 he married Dorothy Mileham, by whom he had ten children, but only one son and a daughter survived their parents. Thomas became a Fellow of the College of Physicians in 1664, was knighted by Charles II in 1671, and died in 1682. His son, Edward, was president of the College of Physicians from 1704 until his death in 1708.

Sir Thomas Browne was well read in contemporary as well as in classical literature. He was an admirer of Harvey and Lower, well acquainted with the works of Sydenham, and corresponded with other leading physicians. Unlike Sydenham, Browne expressed his belief in the value of reading medical works but, like him, he held that experience is more important in the training of a physician. It is assumed that his medical practice was conventional; unfortunately none of his casebooks, if he wrote any, has been preserved.

Religio medici was written about 1635, when Browne was practising in the Yorkshire countryside, and amended from time to time in the manuscript copies lent to his friends. One of these got into the hands of a printer, Andrew Crooke, who printed it, without authority, as an anonymous work. It attracted immediate attention and Sir Kenelm Digby (p. 142) praised it in his *Observations upon Religio medici* (1642). In the same year Browne published a corrected version under his own name. *Religio medici* was a plea for religious toleration in an age when this was sadly lacking, an attempt to resolve the eternal conflict between science and religious dogma, and sundry speculations, all expressed in clear though rather elaborate English. Although only 30 years old when he wrote the book, Browne was already well read and widely travelled and his book expresses a kindly humanitarian philosophy in marked contrast to the diatribes of the warring sects. He says: 'I borrow not the rules of my religion from Rome or from Geneva, but the dictates of my own reason.'[61] He was, however, by no means free from superstition. 'For my own part,' he says, 'I have ever believed and now know that there are witches.'[62] He also believed in the cure of the king's evil by the royal touch.

By 1646 Browne had accumulated numerous notes on popular beliefs and superstitions, which he published as *Pseudoxia epidemica* or, as an English title, *Enquiries into Vulgar and Common Errors*. Nearly 200 topics are dealt with, usually starting with the cause of the error and then presenting the evidence against it. He enquired into such diverse beliefs as whether the phoenix exists, whether swans sing before they die, and whether the right and left legs of badgers are the same length. Browne points out gross errors in the works of Aristotle, Hippocrates, and Galen, and points out too that none of these ancient writers thought himself infallible; only their successors made that claim for them. Browne performed numerous experiments himself to support or disprove popular beliefs but had to rely also on the observations and experiments of other people. In later editions of what was, at the time, his most popular book he took the opportunity to make numerous changes in the light of new knowledge. His conclusion is translated from a Latin maxim, 'The first step in wisdom is to know the false'.[63]

Browne published two other essays in 1658, *Urne Buriall* and *The Garden of Cyrus*. The former ranges from archaeology to meditations on mortality; the latter is a flight of fancy provoked by the arrangement of flower petals and the pattern of Roman orchards, based on the 'quincunx' or letter X. The only observation relevant to medicine is, in *Urne Buriall*, what may be the first description of adipocere, a white, waxy substance into which human flesh may be converted if buried in moist soil.

Browne's 'whole house and garden', according to the diarist, John Evelyn, were 'a paradise and cabinet of rarities, and that of the best collection, especially medals, books, plants and natural things'.[64] He was an outstanding naturalist and a friend and correspondent of John Ray (p. 72) as well as of John Evelyn. He corresponded with the Royal Society but never joined it, probably because it would have been difficult for him to attend the meetings in London. His very wide interests were accompanied by a devout religious faith, expressed in a manuscript published posthumously entitled *Christian Morals*.

Sir John Floyer

John Floyer practised medicine at the end of the seventeenth and the beginning of the eighteenth century but it was essentially the same sort of medicine as practised by John Symcotts about 100 years earlier. Floyer was born in Staffordshire in 1649, the third son of landed gentry, and graduated at Oxford, BA in 1688, MA in 1671, BM in 1674 and DM in 1680. Locke, Halley, and Mayow were among his fellow-students. Floyer's practice was based on Lichfield in Hampshire where, like his father, he became a wealthy land-owner. He married and had two sons, became a justice of the peace and was knighted in 1684 for his political work.[65]

Floyer's first book, *The Touchstone of Medicines* (1687) attempted to classify medicines by taste and smell. Another book, *An Enquiry into the Right Uses and Abuses of the Hot, Cold and Temperate Baths in England* (1697) was popular because it coincided with a revival of spa treatment. His best known book, *A Treatise of the Asthma* (1698) described the symptoms of the disease, from which he himself suffered, attributed them to narrowing of the air passages, and recommended fresh air, a light diet, and avoidance of stress as preventive measures. Floyer still accepted the humoral theory and believed that effervescence of the humours was the cause of asthma.[66] Once a fit of asthma had started, a gentle emetic might be administered but blood-letting should be avoided.[67] Cooling drinks might be administered, such as water with niter and sal ammoniac, or cold beer. Good medicines included syrup of horehound in hyssop water, or centaury, gentian and *Carduus* in small beer. If these were ineffective some asthmatics would benefit from drinking their own urine.[68]

Floyer made one important contribution to scientific medicine in his measurement of the pulse rate. In *The Physician's Pulse-Watch* (1707), he described a watch that ran for sixty seconds and he added pulse frequency to the observations of size, strength, quality, and degree of filling of the artery observed by Galen. He studied the factors which influence the pulse rate but later confused his study with mysticism and metaphysics. Floyer died in 1734.

CHAPTER 3

The Legacy of Earlier Medicine

IT IS RELEVANT to the study of seventeenth-century medicine to note the origin of some early beliefs and practices, which still influenced medicine at this time. Some were discredited by the end of the century, whereas others still influence medicine today. In some respects modern medicine can trace a direct descent from the school of Hippocrates in ancient Greece.

Ancient Medicine

The earliest medical practice, of which records are available, assumed that illness was due to displeasure of the gods or to some other supernatural cause; it could be relieved by practical treatment as well as by propitiation of the gods.[1] Babylonian and Assyrian physicians employed astrology to determine the course and outcome of an illness and employed herbal remedies, some of which were still in use in the seventeenth century; these include aloes, belladonna, cannabis, mandragora, mustard, and poppy.[2] Egyptian medicine developed from Babylonian and Assyrian, and the Ebers papyrus (about 1500 BC) prescribes drugs (and incantations and amulets) for particular diseases. Some of the herbs were described again more than 1500 years later by Dioscorides (p. 71) and some are still in use today, these include castor oil, hyoscine, and senna.[3] Another, still widely used in the seventeenth century but no longer popular, is wormwood (*Artemisia*) for the treatment of digestive and many other disorders.[4]

Greek medicine

The medicine of ancient Greece drew heavily on Egyptian practice but developed a different theory of illness, which was widely accepted throughout the Middle Ages and still influenced medicine in the seventeenth century. The school of Pythagoras (fifth century BC), of which the philosopher and physician, Empedocles, was a leading member, propounded the doctrine that all matter consists of the four 'elements': earth, fire, air and water, and attributed to them the four primary qualities of dryness, heat, cold and wetness.[5] (Fig 5). Earth, for instance, is dry and cold; fire is dry and hot. The body has four fluids (humours) corresponding to the four elements; these are black bile, yellow bile, blood and phlegm. Aristotle (fourth century BC) added the concept of four temperaments: melancholic, choleric, sanguine and phlegmatic, corresponding to the four humours.[6] An individual's mental and physical condition was considered to depend on the balance of these humours; a melancholic person, for instance, has a predominance of black bile; a sanguine person has an excess of blood. This false humoral theory, accepted uncritically by most physicians until the late seventeenth century, greatly hindered the advance of medical science.

Democritus, a younger contemporary of Empedocles, propounded theories, which exercised less influence at the time and in the early seventeenth century but are more in accord with modern scientific thought. He believed that matter consists of indestructible particles (atoms) in perpetual motion, that sensation is due to external stimulation of sense organs, and that the embryo is formed from the seed of both parents.[7]

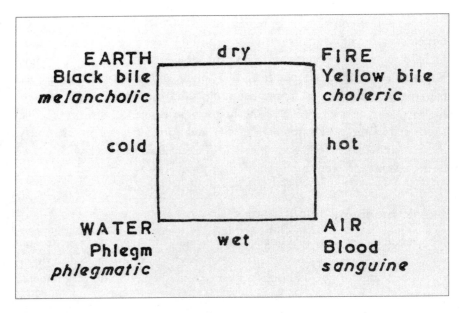

Figure 5. The elements, qualities, humours and temperaments

Hippocrates, the greatest name in the history of medicine, was a Greek, born on the island of Cos about 440 BC. The teaching of the Hippocratic school (the so-called Hippocratic corpus, none of which can be attributed directly to Hippocrates himself) was widely disseminated and much of it survived to be edited, translated, and printed in the sixteenth and later centuries. Medicine and surgery were combined and both were divorced from theology. Disease was assumed to have natural, not supernatural causes, but was still attributed to disorder of the humours. Even the 'sacred disease' (epilepsy), according to Hippocrates, is no more sacred than any other.[8] The surgical part of the Hippocratic corpus, which influenced seventeenth-century surgery is referred to in Chapter 7.

The first 'aphorism' of Hippocrates, a general comment on medical practice, is the best known. 'Life is short and the Art [of medicine] long; the occasion fleeting; experience fallacious, and judgement difficult. The physician must not only be prepared to do what is right himself, but also to make the patient, the attendants and externals co-operate.'[9]

The Hippocratic oath, defining the physician's responsibility to his patient, is still the basis of medical ethics today. It promises, among other things:

> I will use treatment to help the sick according to my ability and judgment, but never with a view to injury and wrongdoing. Neither will I administer a poison to anybody when asked to do so, nor will I suggest such a course . . . Into whatsoever houses I enter I will enter to help the sick and I will abstain from all intentional wrongdoing and harm . . . and whatsoever I shall see or hear in the course of my profession . . . if it be what should not be published abroad, I will never divulge.[10]

In a modern form the oath is still required of students at some universities before qualifying in medicine. Parts of the original oath, now omitted as impracticable or inappropriate, are a promise to teach the art (medicine) without fee to the children of one's teachers, not to procure abortion, and not to cut for the stone. No individual could now teach the whole art to students and, since potential gynaecologists and surgeons as well as physicians now take the oath in the universities which preserve the custom, the last two promises fall away.

Case reports in the Hippocratic corpus are so detailed and accurate that many of the diseases can be recognised today, they include pneumonia, pulmonary tuberculosis, puerperal (childbed) fever, epilepsy, mumps, dysentery and malaria. There are no comparable records for the next 2000 years. Some drugs were employed but the emphasis was on diet, baths and exercise. Nature was regarded as the great healer and the physician's duty was to assist nature. Sometimes this could be achieved by venesection (p. 59) or by cupping (p. 60) on the assumption that blood-letting would remove more of the humour in excess than of the others. Venesection was still very widely practised in the seventeenth century.

In the Hippocratic treatise *Of the Epidemics* particular 'epidemic constitutions' are described, situations in which the place and the weather are responsible for a high incidence of particular diseases;[11] this concept was applied to London by Thomas Sydenham in the seventeenth century (p. 27). Another treatise *The Book of Prognostics*, contains a vivid description of the appearance of a patient dying of fever, the 'Hippocratic facies', which would be known in the seventeenth century and is still recognised today.

A sharp nose, hollow eyes, collapsed temples; the ears cold, contracted, and their lobes turned out: the skin about the forehead being rough, distended and parched; the colour of the whole face being green, black, livid, or lead-coloured, if unexplained by insomnia, diarrhoea or fasting, presages death.[12]

Shortly after the death of Hippocrates a great school of medicine was founded in Alexandria which, like the Hippocratic school, rejected supernatural causes of disease and preferred hygiene to therapy. Diet, exercise, and bathing were preferred to strong drugs and bleeding. The contributions of the leading members of the Alexandrian school to medical science are described in Chapter 5 but one of them, Herophilus, made an important contribution to the practice of medicine by instituting the systematic study of the pulse, which he believed was related to the heart beat.[13] He even counted the pulse rate, using a water clock, a practice which was generally abandoned after his time until it was introduced into England early in the eighteenth century by Sir John Floyer with his pulse watch (p. 34). Another Alexandrian whose influence extended into later centuries was Soranus, who wrote a long *Gynaecology* and a short *Midwives' Catechism* (p. 120).

By the end of the first century BC the Alexandrian School had degenerated into warring sects: dogmatists (emphasising anatomy), empiricists (emphasising philosophy), and methodists (emphasising care of the individual patient).[14] It was the methodists who saved the Hippocratic tradition for later medicine. Much ancient medical writing was lost when the great library at Alexandria was destroyed in Julius Caesar's Egyptian war.

Roman medicine

The earliest medicine in Rome was the worship of the god or goddess associated with the patient's disease. The senior goddess, *Dea Salus*, was responsible for public health. Even when Greek medicine was introduced it was accepted only by the educated upper class, while the majority of the population continued to seek help from the appropriate deity; from the third century BC this was often Asclepius, the Greek god of medicine.

Asclepiades of Bithynia, a Greek philosopher turned physician, had a successful practice in Rome in the second and first centuries BC. He bridged the gap between Greek theoretical and Roman practical medicine. Roman medicine was described in detail more than a century later by Aurelius Cornelius Celsus in *De medicina* (c. AD 30), the earliest scientific work in Latin and one of the first to be printed (in 1478).[15] Celsus was not a physician but a nobleman and an encyclopeadic writer. In this book he discusses diet and hygiene, describes diseases and injuries, and prescribes medical and surgical treatment.

Galen of Pergamon, a Greek who had studied in Alexandria and elsewhere and settled in Rome in the second century AD, saved from oblivion much of the writing of the Hippocratic and other schools by incorporating it in his numerous treatises, which were written in Greek. His views on anatomy and physiology (Chapter 5) and on medicine were translated into Arabic and later into Latin and were accepted almost without question for more than 1500 years. The study of medicine at Oxford and Cambridge in the seventeenth century consisted largely of reading the works of Galen.

Galen accepted the doctrine of the four humours and believed that most illness is due to imbalance of the humours, which can most conveniently be relieved by blood-letting.[16] He also believed that particular drugs purge particular humours. As a practising physician he made extensive use of plant material as drugs, some of which are still in use and may be referred to as 'galenicals'. He is associated also with theriac and an earlier preparation, mithridatium, both originally intended as general antidotes against poisons but widely used by Galen in the treatment of wounds, fractures, and sundry diseases as well as snake-bite. Galen's preparation of theriac was mostly herbal and contained sixty-four ingredients.[17] The original mithridatium probably contained about forty-one ingredients[18] but both were modified later by the physicians prescribing them and might contain as few as four constituents, though usually about a dozen. A common animal constituent of theriac and of mithridatium was castoreum (a secretion of the beaver).[19] Both theriac and mithridatium were still prescribed in the seventeenth century, especially for plague, and although each was already a complex mixture it might become a constituent of another mixture.

Probably the greatest achievement of Roman medicine, even before the time of Galen, was in public health. By the beginning of the Christian Era Rome had a pure water supply, efficient drainage, and strict regulations for disposal of garbage – much better hygiene than seventeenth-century London.[20] The Romans also established hospitals, at first military at strategic points and later for civilians in Rome and provincial towns. The medical staff of these hospitals was employed by the army or by the town and treatment was free. In contrast, leading physicians in private practice charged very high fees.

The Middle Ages

Medicine did not advance in western Europe during the early Middle Ages; instead there was a reversion to belief in supernatural causes of disease, which discouraged attempts at treatment by physical means. Monasteries preserved and copied ancient documents and would-be physicians studied these uncritically and acted on their precepts. Progress in medicine took place mainly in the Arab world, which included at least part of Spain after AD 711.

Islamic medicine

The spread of Islam to occupy the previously Roman empire in Africa by the end of the seventh century, and Islamic toleration of other faiths and encouragement of scholarship, put the Arabs in the forefront of medical theory and practice. Greek medical works, including those of Galen, were translated into Arabic and leading Arab physicians made observations of their own. The Arabs were largely responsible for the emphasis on astrology in medicine and this influence was so profound that, in the seventeenth century, many physicians would consult a patient's horoscope for guidance in the diagnosis, treatment, and prognosis of the illness.

The works of two Persian physicians, Rhazes in the tenth century and Avicenna in the eleventh, written in Arabic and later translated into Latin, were widely studied in Europe and had considerable influence on the practice of medicine for many centuries.

Rhazes was a great physician in the Hippocratic tradition and wrote numerous books, including a *Treatise on Smallpox and Measles*, the first monograph on the subject. He also wrote the first description of hay fever.[21] He had an extensive materia medica and introduced mercury ointment into medical practice, where it later became a standard treatment for syphilis. Other new drugs introduced by Arab pharmacists and prescribed in seventeenth-century England included camphor, cassia, tamarind and aconite.[22]

Avicenna (Ali ibn Sina), the other great Persian physician, was also a philosopher, scientist, and poet. His encyclopaedic *Canon*, described by Sir William Osler as 'the most famous medical textbook ever written',[23] broke new ground in its logical methods of diagnosis and treatment. Disorders described include rabies, meningitis, nephritis, facial paralysis, breast cancer and the effect of various poisons. The *Canon* was translated into Latin in the twelfth century and was a required textbook for medical students until about the middle of the seventeenth century.

European medicine

Salerno, a seaside resort south of Naples, was the site of the first important medical school in western Europe. Founded by Benedictine monks from the nearby monastery on Monte Cassino, it gradually freed itself from their control and by AD 1000 was a lay organisation. The *Antidotarium* of Salerno contained the prescriptions recommended by the school. It was based on Arabic medical works translated into Latin, but also on personal experience, and was revised from time to time. The best known writing of the Salerno school is a poem of unknown authorship, *Regimen sanitatis*, first written probably in the eleventh century and added to thereafter. It deals with many aspects of medicine besides hygiene and was translated in the Middle Ages into French, English, German, Italian, Polish, Czech, Flemish and Hebrew.[24] To date more than 300 editions have been published.

Salerno attracted students from many countries and the school was supported by the emperor, Frederick II, who decreed in 1224 that nobody should practise medicine in his kingdom of the Two Sicilies without first passing an appropriate examination at Salerno. Physicians trained at Salerno carried its teaching to other medical schools in Europe, but Rubin claims that Anglo-Saxon 'leechbooks', based on Latin, Greek, and Germanic sources, were used in England long before Salernitan writings could have reached there.[25] English 'leeches' included clergy and lay practitioners and practised both medicine and surgery. Some monks trained as physicians, but rarely as surgeons because of the edict of the Council of Tours (1163) that a priest must not shed blood (p. 104).

The Church included some crusading orders and, stimulated in 1198 by Pope Innocent III, created hospitals on the route to the Holy Land, in which the sick were tended by members of the order. Rapid spread of leprosy in Europe, especially in the thirteenth century, led to segregation of lepers in leper hospitals, an important factor in the ultimate conquest of the disease, which was much less common by the end of the fourteenth century. It has also been suggested that plague, attacking especially the already infirm, may have played a part in reducing the number of lepers.[26]

Medieval monasteries had infirmaries, in which the elderly, infirm, and sick were cared for, and some of these established herb gardens, but the first English hospitals, in the modern sense of the word, were established in London, St Bartholomew's in 1137 and St Thomas's in 1215. During the thirteenth century hospitals began to pass from ecclesiastical to municipal control and fewer priests practised medicine.

Renaissance And Reformation

The questioning of established authority, which was a feature of the Renaissance, included doubt of the supernatural origin of disease and of the value of astrology in medicine, questions still unsettled in the seventeenth century. There were dramatic advances in medical science (Chapter 5) and some advance in surgery (Chapter 7) but such improvement as took place in medical practice was largely due to reversion to Hippocratic principles.

Syphilis

The Renaissance introduced a new challenge to medicine in 1494, when an epidemic of syphilis started in Naples and spread from there throughout Europe. It was commonly believed that the disease was introduced into Europe by some of Christopher Columbus's men returning from the West Indies in 1493, though sporadic outbreaks of what was probably syphilis occurred in England and in France before this date.

The rapid spread of the epidemic was attributed to the army of Charles VIII of France, which was in Italy at the time and included Spanish mercenaries. The epidemic reached London in 1503 and physicians were at a loss how to treat it because it had not been mentioned by Hippocrates or Galen. Some prescribed an infusion of guiacum (*Lignum vitae*), a wood from the Spanish West Indies, on the principle that since the disease was American the cure should also be American.[27] Although ineffective and very expensive, guiacum was still prescribed for the treatment of syphilis in the first half of the seventeenth century, but later it was usually replaced by mercury ointment.

Although the epidemic of syphilis started in Italy it was known in England as the French disease (*morbus gallicus*). It was also called the great pox because of the large ulcers (gummata) which appear in a later stage of the disease. The name, syphilis, was first introduced in Italy in 1530, when Girolamo Fracastoro published his poem, *Syphilis sive morbus gallicus*, about a shepherd called Syphilus who suffered from the disease; the poem was translated into many languages and published in numerous editions. Fracastoro's other important work, *De contagione et contagiosis morbis* (1546), is the first presentation of the modern concept of transmission of disease germs by contagion or infection;[28] such germs were first recognised by Louis Pasteur in the nineteenth century; few, if any, sixteenth- or seventeenth-century physicians believed in them.

Physicians

Jean Fernel, a Frenchman, was probably the greatest physician of the sixteenth century. He corrected many errors in the works of Galen, described a number of diseases, and correlated the signs and symptoms with post-mortem findings. His *Pathology*, the first medical treatise to use that title, was a systematic study of disease, which rejected the humoral theory.[29] In 1554 he incorporated this and other publications on blood-letting and on physiology in a textbook of medicine, *Medicina*, in which he included 'all that is good and that stands confirmed on a solid basis in the ancient masters and added on his own part what his experience found they had omitted. He removed uncertainties, corrected errors, and excised the superfluous.'[30] At first, like other physicians of the time, Fernel employed astrology in the diagnosis and prognosis of his patients but, unlike the others, he compared the astrological predictions with the actual result and eventually abandoned astrology. This brought him into conflict with other leading physicians of the time and with the very conservative medical faculty of the University of Paris, where he was a professor. Fortunately for Fernel he was physician to King Henry II and enjoyed the protection of his royal patron. Fernel was too much in advance of his time to have much influence on his contemporaries or even on English medicine in the next century.

Paracelsus (Aureolus Theophrastus Bombastus von Hohenheim), a German-Swiss contemporary of Fernel, was an even more outspoken critic of the old regime. Lacking powerful patronage he suffered abuse and even exile for his unorthodox views. Paracelsus studied chemistry in the mines at Schwaz in Austria and then medicine at several European universities, notably those of Vienna and Ferrara. There is no evidence of his graduating as a doctor but he became municipal physician and professor of medicine at Basle before travelling widely in Europe and the Middle East, mostly as an army surgeon.[31] He deplored the distinction between physician and surgeon and believed that a good doctor should be both. Being of a quarrelsome disposition and openly attacking the authority of ancient writers, on which the medicine of the time depended, Paracelsus made many enemies and was driven out of more than one city, leading a wandering life with deteriorating health until he died in Salzburg in 1541 at the age of 48.

Paracelsus believed in astrology and that particular planets are related to particular organs of the body and to particular metals, which can cure diseases of these organs. He also believed in the 'doctrine of signatures' for plants, some medical herbs being identifiable from their shape or colouring as related to a particular organ or disease (p. 61). He accepted the traditional four elements (p. 36) but added three principles: sulphur, mercury, and salt which are combustible, volatile, and residual respectively when heated.[32] He thought that there are different kinds of salt in the body, responsible for different diseases; disease was not due to imbalance of humours.

In 1533, at Schwaz, Paracelsus published a book on miners' diseases, the first treatise on occupational medicine. Most of his writing was published posthumously, the most important chemical treatise, *Archidoxis*, in 1570. Although not the first to prescribe inorganic medicines, Paracelsus is often regarded as the father of the iatrochemical school of physicians (p. 11), which gained strength in England in the seventeenth century, particularly after the publication in 1648 of the *Opera* of the Flemish chemical physician, Jean Baptiste van Helmont. Many of the ideas of Paracelsus have not stood the test of time but some were important advances in medical thinking; he believed in the localisation of disease to particular organs, he sought specific remedies for particular diseases, and he noted that the dose distinguishes a remedy from a poison.[33] Unfortunately in the treatment of syphilis with mercury, which Paracelsus recommended, the remedial dose is also poisonous.

Giovanni Batptista del Monte, at the University of Padua, was responsible about 1545 for a very significant advance in medical teaching. He took his students to the patients' bedside in the local hospital to teach them clinical medicine.[34] The practice lapsed after his death in 1552 but was revived later in the century. In 1630 clinical instruction was introduced at the university of Leyden and in 1634 at Montpellier.[35] In the seventeenth century neither of the English universities offered this form of teaching, which is now regarded as the most important part of the medical curriculum.

Lazare Rivière (Riverius), professor of medicine at the University of Montpellier from 1622 to 1655, wrote a comprehensive *Praxis medicinae* (1640), which was translated into English in 1655 by Nicholas Culpeper and others.[36] Rivière introduced the study of chemistry into the medical curriculum and his use of inorganic as well as plant remedies encouraged the English iatrochemists.

Tudor England

Common diseases

Diagnosis, as we know it today, was impracticable in Tudor England because there was no concept of specific diseases due to particular infective agents and metabolic disorders were unknown. Some sets of symptoms were sufficiently striking to constitute a disease entity, especially in epidemic diseases such as plague or smallpox or where the presenting symptom was obvious, as in the bloody flux (dysentery) or the falling sickness (epilepsy).

Other diseases prevalent at the time were syphilis, typhus, and malaria, and there were at least ten epidemics of plague in England during the sixteenth century.[37] Leprosy, common in the Middle Ages, was dying out in England by the end of the fifteenth century but a strange disease, the sweating sickness, deserves special mention because it was restricted to the Tudor period and most of the epidemics were confined to England.[38] The sweating sickness broke out in five major epidemics between 1485 and 1551. Only one of these (in 1528) spread to the continent of Europe. The disease was characterised by headache, pain in the chest, and profuse sweating, and often proved fatal within twenty-four hours. The mortality was very high; in one epidemic the Venetian ambassador estimated that

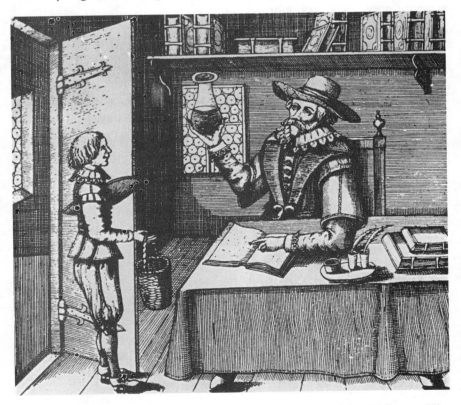

Figure 6. Uroscopy. From a 17th-century book (courtesy of the Wellcome Historical Medical Library, London)

5000 died of the disease in one week in London.[39] The cause is still unknown.

Diagnosis

Diagnosis of disease might depend on the pseudo-sciences of astrology or uroscopy (Fig 6). The urine flask was as much the symbol of the physician in Tudor times as the stethoscope is today. For uroscopy a twelve-hour sample of urine was collected in a glass flask of a particular shape and taken to the physician for inspection. In the early Tudor period it might not be considered necessary to see the patient; the treatment was based on uroscopy and on the patient's symptoms and horoscope. Physical examination was regarded as unnecessary and even the galenic practice of feeling the pulse was often ignored. The study of the pulse was revived as Hippocratic methods were re-introduced[40] and the coat of arms granted to the College of Physicians in 1546 depicts a hand feeling a pulse.

Treatment

Medical treatment usually involved blood-letting and drugs, prescribed by the physician and dispensed by the apothecary. Although the sixteenth-century apothecary was not legally qualified to prescribe medicine but only to dispense and sell it, he would often do this without a physician's prescription, which his poorer customers could not afford. The dispute about the apothecary's right to provide medicine without prescription continued into and throughout the seventeenth century.

Most prescriptions of the time contained many constituents. Theriac, originally intended as an antidote to poisons (p. 39), was prescribed in Tudor and Stuart times for a variety of diseases, including plague (p. 153). Most plant drugs (galenicals) were ineffective or merely purgative but opium was known and used. Components of animal origin were numerous and bizarre, including the blood of various animals from toad to bull (turtle blood being especially popular), the bile of some animals, the liver and brain of others, and such odd medicaments as powdered pearl or unicorn's horn; this last was particularly valuable and expensive, possibly because there is no such creature. It is possible that what was sold as unicorn's horn was the long, twisted horn of a marine mammal, the narwhal (*Monodon monoceros*), but merchants steamed and twisted ivory, wood, and other materials into counterfeit horn.[41]

Physicians

Thomas Linacre studied Greek at Oxford before studying medicine and graduating MD 'with the highest praise' at Padua.[42] On his return to England he incorporated his degree at both Oxford and Cambridge and settled in Oxford to teach Greek and practise medicine. One of his important contributions to medicine was to translate many of Galen's works directly from Greek into Latin, thereby correcting many of the errors which had crept in when the only Latin versions were translations from Arabic. In 1501 he became domestic physician to King Henry VII and he continued in the post of royal physician under Henry VIII. In 1518 he persuaded the king to grant a charter for the foundation of the College of Physicians and he was the first president of the College. By this time he had been ordained as a priest but he remained in office as president of the College of Physicians until his death in 1524.

John Caius, a graduate of Cambridge and Padua and another distinguished classical scholar, was physician to Edward VI, Mary I, and Elizabeth I and president of the College of Physicians. He was a very successful practitioner but found time to give a course of lectures on anatomy to surgeons at the Barbers' Hall and was instrumental in introducing the subject into the medical curriculum at Oxford and Cambridge.[43] He wrote *De medendi methodo* (1544), supporting Galenic methods of treatment and also a dramatic account of the last epidemic of sweating sickness in 1551.

Andrew Boorde studied medicine at Montpellier, incorporated his degree at Oxford, and treated many of the English aristocracy. His *Breviary of Helthe* (1547), deals with medical and surgical training and practice and was still a popular textbook in the seventeenth century. A physician, he believed, should first be educated in the *trivium* (grammar, rhetoric and dialectic) and the *quadrivium* (arithmetic, geometry, astronomy and music) but, for a surgeon, a good eye and a steady hand are more important; a surgeon should be versed in astrology and in serious cases should consult a physician.[44] Common disorders are listed in alphabetical order and the appropriate treatment for each is prescribed; this usually involves bloodletting, purging, and administration of herbal medicines. Sometimes, as in dysentery, epilepsy, and gout, dietary restrictions are recommended. Among the many disorders described are the two forms of madness recognised in the sixteenth and seventeenth centuries, mania and melancholy. It is interesting to note that the treatment of both included an extract of *Cassia fistula*,[45] a tropical plant indigenous to India and probably imported from the Far East before the days of the British East India Company.

Thomas Phaire wrote the first English textbook of paediatrics, *The Boke of Chyldren* (1545), which was still popular in the seventeenth century. It lists the common diseases of children and prescribes the remedies. Most of these are herbal but parts of animals or their dung are sometimes included and occasionally inorganic material.[46] Phaire writes: 'My purpose is here to doo thyme good that have moste nede, that is to saye children.'[47]

Regulation of medical practice

At the beginning of the sixteenth century trained and qualified medical practitioners were greatly outnumbered by untrained and unqualified quacks, whose practice was regarded by the authorities as dangerous to the health of those whom they treated. The first attempt to set a standard of medical training in England was an Act of 1511, which decreed that no one should practise medicine or surgery in London or for seven miles around it without first being examined and approved by four experienced physicians or surgeons and licensed by the Bishop of London or the Dean of St Paul's.[48] Outside the London area licences to practise were the responsibility of the bishop of the diocese, acting on the recommendation of advisers who were not necessarily doctors. Graduates of the universities of Oxford or Cambridge were entitled to practise anywhere in England. Although these regulations were still in force in the seventeenth century they did little to eliminate the horde of quacks, who practised illegally and usually without interference.

The next step in raising the status of the profession was the creation of the College of Physicians by Henry VIII in 1518, with authority to regulate the practice of medicine in the London area. The College granted, after examination, a licence to practise, but a candidate for Fellowship of the College had to be a Doctor of Medicine.[49] Since the number of Fellows was limited by statute, though it was increased from time to time, a category of Candidate was introduced for those eligible for Fellowship when a place fell vacant. The College tried unsuccessfully in the sixteenth and again in the seventeenth century to gain control of medical practice throughout England.

CHAPTER 4

The Practice of Medicine

Common diseases

IN THE EARLY SEVENTEENTH CENTURY the ancient concept of illness as an imbalance of the humours (p. 36) was still generally accepted but a greater variety of ailments was recognised. The diseases described by Walter Bruel in his *Praxis medicinae* (1632) include: apoplexy, arthritis (including gout), asthma, *calculus renum* (kidney stone), cholera, diabetes, dysentery, epilepsy, *gallicus morbus* (syphilis), haemorrhoids, mania, *morbus regius* (the king's evil), plague, pleurisy and worms. Also considered as diseases are a number of conditions which we should now regard as symptoms or signs of disease, such as aurigo (jaundice), dropsy (oedema), headache, paralysis, syncope (fainting), tussis (cough), and vertigo. Excessive and suppressed menstruation are described, as are lethargy, melancholy, and nightmare. Some diseases which were common and recognised at the time, including ague (malaria), gaol fever (typhus), scurvy, and smallpox, are not mentioned in Bruel's book, though they are in others.

The major epidemic diseases of the century were plague, smallpox, and typhus, and possibly influenza (Chapter 10). Leprosy had virtually disappeared in England[1] but the French pox (syphilis), though no longer epidemic, was still widespread in all ranks of society. It is highly probable that Charles II suffered from syphilis and almost certain that James II had the disease.[2] Syphilis is transmitted by sexual intercourse or by an infected mother to her baby. Misunderstanding of its nature was due not only to ignorance of the micro-organism responsible (*Treponema pallidum*), which was not discovered until 1905, but also to the long delay between the first sign of syphilis, a hard sore (chancre) on the genitals, and the later signs (some of them years later) in almost every part of the body but particularly in skin, joints, and nervous system. Another element of confusion was gonorrhoea, a more acute venereal disease due to a different organism (*Neisseria gonorrhoeae*), which might be transmitted at the same time and was not generally recognised as a separate disease until the nineteenth century.

Another very common disease at the time, especially in marshy districts, was ague (malaria). This condition, then thought to be due to noxious vapours, is caused by infection with a micro-organism (*Plasmodium*), transmitted by the bite of a mosquito (*Anopheles*). In tertian malaria, caused by *P. vivax*, fever occurs every second day; in quartan, caused by *P. malaria*, it occurs every third day.

By the end of the century, as a result of the work of medical scientists, most medical practitioners, though not the general public, attributed disease to natural rather than supernatural causes. Many individual diseases had been identified and described by Thomas Sydenham and others, though there was little advance in understanding the causes of disease.

Diagnosis

At the beginning of the century diagnosis was based largely on the medieval practices of uroscopy and astrology.

Uroscopy

Uroscopy was practised as in Tudor times (p. 47), though diagnosis on uroscopy alone, without seeing the patient, was expressly forbidden by the College of Physicians.[3] The doctor would note the smell of the urine, the appearance of the sediment (if any), and the swim (most of the urine), the cloud (which might be present), and the crown (the top).[4] Abnormal constituents such as blood, bile, pus, or gravel might be seen. It was assumed that the urine would be different for men, women and children and for people of different temperament because the proportion of the humours would be different, and it was noted (correctly) that the volume depended on the intake of fluid that day and the day before. By mid seventeenth century uroscopy was falling into disfavour; the physician, James Primrose, derided the pretensions of 'Pisse-prophets' and claimed that they defrauded the public, since disease could not be diagnosed by uroscopy.[5]

Astrology

Although astrology, as an aid to diagnosis, had been discredited by Jean

Fernel in the sixteenth century (p. 44) it was still widely used; indeed it might be considered more important to cast a patient's horoscope than to see him. Diagnosis by astrology, depending on knowledge of the patient's zodiacal sign and of the position of the moon and planets at the time the symptoms appeared, was described in detail by Andrews in *The Astrological Physitian* (1656). The constellations of the zodiac and the planets were thought to govern different parts of the body and particular diseases.[6] For instance Saturn was thought to be cold and dry, corresponding to melancholy and the spleen and associated with gout and apoplexy; if in the constellation of Taurus it promoted the king's evil. Jupiter was regarded as hot and moist, representing the blood and associated with disease of the liver or lungs; if in Capricorn it was associated with diseases of the head. Mars was believed to be hot and dry, as is the sun; their positions in the zodiac corresponded to particular diseases. Venus and the moon represented the remaining combination of properties, cold and moist, and they were associated with diseases of the reproductive system. The moon was also related to the falling sickness and to lunacy. Mercury, like Saturn, was thought to be cold and dry, but its association was with madness. The patient's horoscope could reveal not only the nature but also the probable outcome of the illness. It might also indicate which herbs would cure it; for instance *Carduus benedictus* (holy thistle), being a herb of Mars under Aries, would help vertigo and jaundice and should cure the French pox (syphilis) by antagonism to Venus, which governs that disease.[7] English astrological medicine was at its peak during the Civil Wars and the Interregnum but had ceased to be influential by the end of the century.[8]

Case history

As well as the date of birth, from which the horoscope could be derived, the patient's sex, occupation, and place of residence would be ascertained, the history of the illness noted, and the patient asked about diet, bowel actions, and physical activity.

Physical examination

The pulse would be felt to determine the rhythm and strength of the beat, as recommended by Galen (p. 39), but little attention was paid to the rate until after Floyer's description of the 'pulse-watch' in the eighteenth century (p. 34). Inspection of the patient might reveal the nature and severity of the illness, especially if the signs included a typical rash or superficial swellings. The main purpose of palpation (feeling) was to determine whether the patient was hot, cold, moist, or dry (Aristotle's four qualities); it could also detect abnormal masses in the abdomen and localise areas of tenderness. The other techniques of modern clinical investigation, tapping the chest to ascertain the condition of the lungs and the position and size of the heart (percussion) and listening to heart and breath sounds in the chest (auscultation) had still to be invented.

Descriptions of Disease

The most meticulous observations of illness in the seventeenth century were made by Thomas Sydenham (p. 22) but other physicians also gave clear descriptions, still recognisable today, of particular diseases. It is appropriate to deal with them alphabetically since that was the usual practice in seventeenth-century medical writing. Major epidemic diseases are described in a later chapter (Chapter 10).

Ague

Ague (malaria) is caused by a micro-organism (*Plasmodium*) transmitted by the bite of a mosquito (*Anopheles*) (p. 147). Sydenham gives a confused and erroneous explanation of the disease but, as usual, his clinical description is vivid.

> All Agues begin with Shivering and Shaking, and are presently succeeded by Heat, and then Sweat; the Sick most commonly vomits both in the cold and hot Fit, is very sick, dry and thirsty, and his Tongue is very dry, and the like: all which Symptoms retreat by degrees as the Sweat comes on; and when it is very plentiful, the Fit seems to be at an end, and he that was just now sick seems to be very well till the Fit returns at its wonted Time, *viz*. a Quotidian once every natural Day, a Tertian every other Day, a Quartan every third Day, reckoning from the beginning of one Fit to the beginning of the next.[9]

Apoplexy

Apoplexy (commonly referred to nowadays as a 'stroke') is due to blockage or rupture of a cerebral blood vessel with consequent damage to the brain. A common result is paralysis of the limbs and some loss of sensation on one side of the body (hemiplegia). Since most nerve paths to and from trunk and limbs cross in the brain stem, damage to one side of the brain causes paralysis of the opposite side of the body. In spite of Willis's published work on the brain and cerebral blood vessels (p. 77) the condition was not understood in the seventeenth century and descriptions of it are vague. 'The *Apoplexy* is a consternation of the Mind with the loss of outward senses and motion. The *part affected* is the Brain with his Nerves.'[10] A better description is 'a sudden loss of movement and sense'.[11] Affecting one side of the body it is palsy (hemiplegia). The palsy may be gradual in onset, affecting motion or sense or both, and is prolonged.[12]

Asthma

Asthma is difficulty in breathing due to narrowing of the air passages; it is often associated with sensitivity to foreign protein (allergy), a phenomenon not recognised until the twentieth century. Although asthma was described in the Ebers papyrus about 1500 BC and in many subsequent publications the first English monograph on the subject was by Sir John Floyer (p. 34), a physician who suffered from the condition. He found inspiration difficult and expiration easier, though slow and sometimes wheezing.[13] This conflicts with our experience today that there is more obstruction to expiration, when the small air passages are narrower. Floyer observed that a fit might last three or four days (*status asthmaticus*) and end with coughing of blood-stained sputum or even prove fatal. The country physician, John Symcotts, noted the danger of a severe attack (p. 30).

Diabetes

The 'pissing evil' (diabetes mellitus) was recognised in early Hindu medicine, when the excessive output of urine, foul breath, and languor were noted, as well as the sweet taste of the urine.[14] Although the condition was described again by Willis and other seventeenth-century physicians no significant advance in understanding the disease occurred before the twentieth century.

Dysentery

Bacillary dysentery, the commonest type, is an acute infection of the bowel leading to severe diarrhoea, usually with blood and mucus in the stools (the 'bloody flux'). The condition is described by Sydenham as well as by

Bruel, but neither was aware that epidemics of dysentery are due to contamination of food or drinking water from infected stools. The organism responsible, *Shigella,* is a bacterium discovered by Kiyoshi Shiga in 1897.[15]

Epilepsy

Epilepsy (the falling sickness) is still not fully understood, although it is known to be associated with abnormal electrical activity of the brain. The usual pattern of an epileptic fit (*grand mal*) involves convulsions and foaming at the mouth.[16] Bruel gives a graphic description of an attack.

> When hee is deprived of his senses hee falls to the ground with a violent shaking of his body, his face is wrested [twisted], his eyes turned upwards, his chinne is sometimes driven to his shoulders, and oftentimes he voideth feed, ordure, urine against his will . . . they do often snort and cry out in their sleepe . . . they oftentimes thrust out their toungs [*sic*], and it is to bee feared, that sometime they bite them with their teeth.[17] There is likewise a gentler kinde of falling sicknesse [petit mal], which doth not differ much from giddiness.[18]

Gout

Gout is a metabolic disorder characterised by acute pain and swelling of a joint or joints, most commonly of the big toe. According to Sydenham, who suffered from the disease:

> The Gout most commonly seizes such old Men as have liv'd the best part of their Lives tenderly and delicately, allowing themselves freely Banquets, Wine, and other spirituous Liquors: and at length, by reason of the Sloth that always attends old Age, have quite omitted such Exercises as young Men are wont to use.[19] He goes to bed and sleeps well; but about two a-clock in the Morning is awakened by the Pain, seizing either his great Toe, the Heel, the Calf of the Leg, or the Ancle: this Pain is like that of dislocated Bones, with the Sense, as it were of Water almost cold, poured upon the Membranes of the Parts affected: presently shivering and shaking follow with a feverish Disposition. The Pain is first gentle, but encreases by degrees . . . moreover, the part affected has such a quick and exquisite Pain, that it is not able to bear the weight of the Clothes upon it. There are a thousand fruitless Endeavours used to ease the Pain, by changing the Place continually, whereon the Body and the affected Members lie;

yet there is no Ease to be had, till two or three a-clock in the Morning (a Night and a Day being spent from the first approach of the Fit), at which time the Sick has sudden Ease.[20]

The symptoms recur, often affecting the other foot, and relapses are common.

Pleurisy

Pleurisy (inflammation of the membranes between lung and chest wall) is commonly associated with pneumonia (inflammation of the lung). Sydenham observed that it frequently affects 'Country People and those accustomed to hard Labour'.

> It ordinarily begins with a Shaking and Shivering, and then Heat, Thirst, Restlessness, and other Symptoms of a Fever follow . . . After a few hours . . . the Patient is taken with a violent pricking Pain in one of his Sides about the Ribs . . . he coughs frequently, which occasions great Pain by reason of the Disturbance of the inflamed Parts, so that sometimes he holds his Breath to prevent Coughing. The Matter which is spit up at the beginning of the Disease is little and thin, and often mixed with particles of blood.[21]

In a favourable case expectoration becomes more profuse and the other symptoms remit; if this does not happen the illness may prove fatal.[22]

Rickets

Francis Glisson observed that rickets starts in childhood and he provided the first detailed description of the disease (p. 16). He noted that the bony deformities persist into adult life.

St Vitus's dance

The irregular involuntary movements of St Vitus's dance, now associated with rheumatic fever, were dramatically described by Sydenham (Sydenham's chorea).

> *Chorea Sancti Viti* is a sort of Convulsion, which chiefly invades Boys and Girls from ten Years of Age to Puberty. First it shows itself by a certain Lameness, or other Instability of one of the Legs, which the Patient drags after him like a Fool; afterwards it appears in the Hand of the same Side, which he that is affected with this Disease can by no means keep in the same Posture for one Moment . . . If a Cup

of Drink be put into his Hand he represents a thousand Gestures, like Juglers, before he brings it to his Mouth . . . till at length happily reaching his Lips, he flings it suddenly into his Mouth and drinks it greedily.[23]

Scurvy

Scurvy, which is due to lack of vitamin C, was described by Gideon Harvey in 1675 as a new disease (the Disease of London), though it had been known for at least four centuries, when a French priest, Jacques de Vitry, involved in the Crusades, described the condition:

> A sudden pain seized the feet and legs; immediately afterwards the gums and teeth were attacked by a sort of gangrene, and the patient could not eat any more. Then the bones of the leg became horribly black, and so, after having suffered continued pain, during which they showed the greatest patience, a large number of Christians went to rest on the bosom of the Lord.[24]

No better description was offered in the seventeenth century, though Thomas Willis included in his *Practice of Physick* (1684) *A Treatise of the Scurvy*. He thought it was a disease of the blood due to bad air, prolonged fever, heredity, and contagion.[25]

Stone

Renal calculus (stone) was common in the seventeenth century and every physician had prescriptions for treating the condition, though it was usually relieved only by surgery. According to Bruel:

> The stone in the kidneys is a hard substance, bred like unto a stone of sandstone in the substance of the reynes [kidneys], from whence by the force of the urine it is often conveyed thorow the straight pipes into the bladder, if it be not too great; which doth so stretch the passages of the urine that great paine doth follow; and if through weakness of the urine it cannot be brought out, it growes bigger, and as it doth increase, so the paine doth likewise increase . . . This disease doth differ from the colicke for that doth straggle over the whole region of the belly, but in this disease the paine is much more settled.[26]

Barrough noted that the urine might be scanty and bloody and the pain severe.[27]

Syphilis

The French pox (syphilis) was a common ailment in the seventeenth century and was recognised though not understood (p. 42). Barrough noted that the early symptoms included lassitude and fleeting pains and sometimes local ulcer and swollen glands.[28] Later symptoms included large, persistent ulcers (gummata) and severe pains. Sydenham described the primary sore (chancre), which develops at the site of infection, in men commonly the glans of the penis:

> A Spot first like the Measles coming out . . . The said Pustle [pustule] turns at length to an Ulcer . . . which eats daily deeper and wider, and the lips become callous and hard . . . Other symptoms presently follow this; at first a great Sense of Pain in the Yard [penis] as often as it is erected . . . There is moreover a Heat of Urine.[29]

Later symptoms include headache, severe pains in the limbs, and rashes on the skin. Outgrowths of bone develop and degenerate.

> Ulcers seize various parts of the Body, and most commonly begin in the Throat, and are propagated by degrees to the Cartilage of the Nose, thro the Palate and soon consume it; so that wanting its Supporter it falls. The Ulcers and Pain increasing daily, the Sick is devour'd by the Ulcers and Putrefaction, so that he lives a grievous Life by reason of the Pain, Stink, and Scandal, which is much worse than any Death; but at last one Member rotting after another the torn carcass is hid under ground, being very odious before to all above.[30]

The nervous disorders of late syphilis, irregular gait (locomotor ataxy) and insanity (general paralysis of the insane) were not recognised in the seventeenth century.

Worms

Barrough noted that worm infestation is commoner in children than in adults and that worms may be round, flat, or threadlike. Roundworms (*Ascaris*) cause general symptoms, flatworms (*Taenia*) cause wasting, and threadworm (*Enterobius*) cause intense itching in the anal region.[31]

Treatment

In the seventeenth, as in the twentieth century, most patients wanted their doctor to prescribe some treatment for them. It took courage on the part of the doctor to refuse to prescribe when he thought no available treatment would help the condition. William Harvey was reluctant to prescribe medicines unless he believed they would be useful (p. 15) and Thomas Sydenham sometimes refused to do so, saying: 'I have consulted my patient's safety and my own reputation most effectively *by doing nothing at all*'.[32]

Blood-letting

Most patients would expect to have some blood withdrawn as part of the treatment for most ailments. Since disease was generally believed to be due to imbalance of the humours of the body (p. 36) it was logical to draw blood in the hope that more of the humour in excess than of the others would be lost. Many years after William Harvey's discovery of the circulation the site from which blood was taken was still regarded as important. The usual procedure was venesection (Fig 7), a vein being incised with a sharp knife and the blood collected in a convenient receptacle. For disorders of the head a vein of the head or neck would be

Figure 7. Venesection. From a 17th-century print (courtesy of the Wellcome Historical Medical Library, London)

chosen (if the surgeon were sufficiently skilled), for the chest a vein of the upper limb and for the abdomen a vein of the lower limb. Alternatively, the appropriate site could be determined by the patient's horoscope. The amount of blood to be withdrawn depended on the clinical judgment of the physician and the procedure could be repeated frequently. The physician would not normally perform the venesection himself unless there was no surgeon available.

William Harvey accepted blood-letting as 'foremost among all the general remedial means',[33] and Thomas Sydenham complained that plentiful bleeding, though desirable, was not always possible 'by reason of the frowardness of the By-standers, who being possess'd with vain Prejudices would not suffer me to take away a due quantity of Blood'.[34] One may speculate whether the vain prejudices of the bystanders or of the physician would be more harmful to the patient.

William Cole would withdraw as much as three pints of blood at a time from a patient with apoplexy 'if the pulse fail not'[35] but Gideon Harvey, an outspoken critic of the conventional methods of the time, pointed out that bleeding may cause a strong man to faint and is even more dangerous for an ill one. He went so far as to say: 'More owe their Deaths to Physicians than are presently cured by them.'[36] In his opinion the poor had a better chance of recovery because they could not afford physicians or apothecaries.

In contrast to Cole, Paul Barbette considered venesection undesirable in apoplexy; he also thought it should be avoided in dysentery.[37] Floyer found it useless in asthma.[38] Both Willis and Sydenham, who treated almost every ailment with venesection, avoided it in the treatment of gout.

An alternative method of blood-letting was cupping. After scarification of an area of skin a hot hollow vessel was applied to it, blood being drawn into the vacuum as the vessel cooled. Cupping was much less common than venesection and was used for its supposedly beneficial local action.

The application of leeches to draw blood, although practised from very early times, was not common in seventeenth-century England. It became more popular in the eighteenth century, when venesection was less fashionable. The country doctor, John Symcotts (p. 29), employed venesection, cupping and leeches.

Drugs

Blood-letting was often accompanied by the administration of vomits (emetics), purges (purgatives) or clysters (enemas), the general principle being the same, *viz.* to restore the balance of the humours by removing more of the one which was present in excess. Most emetics and purgatives were of plant origin and fairly safe but tartar emetic (antimony potassium tartrate), a highly toxic inorganic compound, was prescribed by some physicians.

Every medical practitioner had his favourite drugs, which he would prescribe for particular diseases or as a general panacea. Most were derived from plants, though some were of animal origin and the inorganic remedies of the iatrochemists (p. 45) were becoming more popular. Some of these were included in the *Pharmacopoea Londinensis* (p. 5); in the 1683 edition Culpeper describes the preparations recommended by the College of Physicians and adds his own comments and criticism. The catalogue includes roots, bark, leaves, flowers, fruits and seeds of numerous plants, mostly indigenous wild flowers. Animals in the catalogue include earthworms, grasshoppers, vipers and woodlice; parts of animals include sparrow's brains, crab's eyes, frog's liver, man's skull and the greatly prized unicorn's horn. Another category, 'Belonging to the sea', includes pearls, sea sand and spermaceti. Finally 'metals and stones' include bezoar (a concretion from the stomach of a ruminant), brimstone (sulphur), diamond, gold, lead, ruby and topaz. Preparations include spirits, tinctures, syrups, powders, electuaries (powders mixed with honey or syrup), pills, trochees (lozenges), oils, ointments and plasters. Methods of preparation are given in considerable detail and a general introduction indicates how treatment should be modified in terms of the four temperaments and the importance of astrology in selecting the appropriate remedy.

Not only astrology but also the 'doctrine of signatures' might guide the physician in his choice of a herbal remedy. Some physical feature of the plant would indicate its medicinal use. Trefoil would be prescribed for heart disease, liverwort for liver disease, and cyclamen for ear disease because, in each case, the leaf is the shape of the affected organ. Also, on the basis of similarities, eyebright, having a spot like an eye, should cure eye diseases, and celandine, having a yellow juice, was prescribed for the treatment of jaundice.

As a rule several compound remedies were prescribed for each complaint.

Some were classified by Bruel as 'preparers' (various drugs), 'emptiers' (emetic, purge or enema), 'averters' (more drugs and sometimes local friction or cupping), and 'strengtheners' (tonics). Particular compound remedies might be prescribed for particular actions, such as 'stayers of the flux' in dysentery, 'expellers of the venom' in plague, 'provokers of the moneths' for failure to menstruate, 'drivers out of wormes', and 'breakers and drivers out of the stone'.

Thomas Sydenham, the leading physician of the age, treated fevers with a variety of remedies, including the bleeding, emetics, and purgatives, which were his basic treatment for most ailments. A favourite emetic was the following: 'Take of *Vinum Benedictum* six Drams; of *Oxymel of Squill* and compound Syrup of *Scabious*, each half an Ounce: mingle them, make a Vomit'.[39] A purgative included two drugs (senna and rhubarb) still used as purgatives today. An enema to stop diarrhoea was as follows:

Take of the Bark of Pomegranats half an Ounce, of Red Roses two Pugils [pinches], boil them in a sufficient Quantity of Cow's Milk, dissolve half an Ounce of Diascordium [a complex herbal mixture containing opium] in half a Pint of the strained Liquor; mingle them, and make a Glister. [clyster=enema.][40]

Some of Sydenham's prescriptions included expensive items such as gold, pearls and bezoar stone, but he cannot have regarded these as essential.

When I was Call'd to a poor Body who was not able to be at the Charge of going through a long course of Physick, I did nothing after Bleeding and Purging were over, if they were indicated, but order them to keep their Beds all the time of their Sickness, and to drink Oatmeal and Barly Broths and the like; and that they should drink moderately small Beer, warm'd to quench their thirst.

Enemas were administered 'and so, without more ado, except that I used to give a gentle Purge at the end of the disease, I cured them'.[41] Ague (malaria) was treated effectively with Peruvian bark (containing quinine), which had been introduced into Europe in 1636 but was not included in the *Pharmacopoea Londinensis* until 1677. For patients, who could not afford this (very expensive) remedy: 'Take of Virginian Snake-weed finely powder'd one Scruple, of White-wine three Ounces; mingle them, let the Sick take it two Hours before the Fit, let him sweat three or four Hours, and let it be repeated twice when the Fit approaches.'[42]

Since gout was not relieved by the routine treatment of bleeding, purging, and sweating Sydenham prescribed a mixture of herbs:

Take of the Roots of Angelica, of the sweet smelling Flag, of Masterwort, Elicampane, of the leaves of common Wormwood, of the Lesser Centaury, of white Hore-Hound, of Germander, of Ground-pine, of Scordium, of common Calaminth, of Feverfew, of Field-Saxi-frage, St John's Wort, Golden-rod, Thyme, Mint, Sage, Rue, *Carduus benedictus*, Penny-royal, Southern-wood, of the Flowers of Camomile, Tansy, Lilley of the Vallies, *English* saffron, of the Seeds of Treacle-Mustard, Garden Scurvy-grass, Caraways, Juniper-Berries, each a suffi-cient Quantity: let the Herbs and Flowers and Roots be gathered when they have most vertue in them; let them be dried and kept in paper Bags till they be finely poudered, to six Ounces of each well mixed, add a sufficient quantity of purify'd Honey and Canary Wine to make an Electuary: take two Drams Morning and Evening.[43]

A similar elaborate herbal mixture might be prescribed by almost any physician for almost any complaint.

For the gonorrhoea, which often preceded the first signs of syphilis and which Sydenham, unlike most of his contemporaries, regarded as a different disease, his treatment was mostly purgation. For the established French pox (syphilis) there were various remedies, the most effective being the application of mercury ointment in sufficient dosage for the absorbed mercury to cause salivation (a sign of mercury poisoning); other compli-cations of this treatment were diarrhoea and ulceration of the gums.

For quinsy (peritonsillar abscess) Sydenham prescribed a gargle less repulsive than many prescriptions of the time. 'Take of Plantain-water and red Rose-water and of the Water of Frogs-spawn, each four Ounces; the Whites of three Eggs turned into Water by beating; of white Sugar-candy three Drams: make a gargarism [gargle].'[44]

John Pechey, who translated some of Sydenham's books into English and wrote *The English Herbal of Physical Plants* (1694), also prescribed remedies of animal origin. He recommended the external application of animal dung for inflammation or dropsy and, internally, dead spiders for ague, ants for palsy or gout, and cat's blood for epilepsy. The Herbal describes only 'such plants as grow in England and are not commonly known; for I thought it needless to trouble the reader with the description of those that every woman knows or keeps in her garden.'[45]

Thomas Willis, though an innovator in science (p. 77), was a traditional physician. The fifty clinical records of his patients which have survived (p. 18), throw light on his conventional treatment. His cases include relief of urinary stone in a boy of 10 with a mixture of white tartar, millipedes, terebinth, mineral waters, and cherry wine. A 10-month-old boy was cured of worms with mercury and a julep. An elderly woman with acute bronchitis was cured with enemas, bleeding, crabs' eyes, and diascordium. A young woman with premenstrual tension was treated successfully with gentle purges and exercise.

Willis treated most fevers with emetics, purges and bleeding. He found that Peruvian bark (p. 147) was particularly effective against the ague (malaria), which was prevalent in Oxford at that time. His prescription for epilepsy included peony, mistletoe, rue, powdered elk's hoof and man's skull, amber and coral.[46] If this failed an amulet of peony root might be hung round the patient's neck. Barrough was another physician who recommended this.[47] For asthma Willis prescribed hartshorn (the powdered antler of a hart)[48] but Floyer, who suffered from the disease (p. 34), derived most benefit from squill (*Scilla*).[49]

John Symcotts, the country doctor (p. 29), prescribed a variety of emetics and purgatives, two traditional complex mixtures, mithridate (p. 40) and theriac (p. 39), *terra sigillata* (sacred sealed earth, ostensibly from the isle of Lemnos), bezoar stone (p. 61), and numerous herbs. 'A medicine to cure the dropsy' contained bryony roots steeped in ale, to which were added brown bread, aniseed, liquorice, honey and butter.[50] A lady with a pimpled face was advised to take syrup of squill with a posset drink. 'It wrought both forwards and backwards with her and cured her.'[51]

Although many purgatives were prescribed, prescriptions for the relief of diarrhoea were less common. Symcotts prescribed

> for the looseness. Take a pint of running water and put thereto three sticks of cinnamon, pomegranate pills, two or three pieces of large mace, a piece of white bread and seethe this together well. Take a quarter of a pound of almonds, wipe them clean and grind them in a mortar and take the liquor to make almond milk and so drink it.[52]

Noah Biggs, known only by his book, *The Vanity of the Craft of Physick* (1621), differed from almost all his contemporaries in rejecting purgation, blood-letting, baths, sweating 'and other practices which diminish body strength'.[53] He doubted the value of all available drugs but thought the future lay with the development of chemical remedies. Biggs believed that the doctrine of signatures (p. 61) is false, that herbs are not related to signs of the zodiac, that simples (medicines composed of a single constituent) are preferable to complex mixtures, that gold and gems are useless in treatment, and that most preparations of bezoar stone and of pearls sold by apothecaries were not genuine.[54] Biggs was so far ahead of his time that little attention was paid to his views.

Other methods of treatment

As well as prescribing drugs and letting blood the physician might advise about clothing and diet, sometimes about limitation of sexual activity, and rarely about exercise. Primrose considered diet very important. 'In health a full diet doth encrease strength, a moderate preserves it, and a spare diet doth diminish it.'[55] He believed that the diet should, as recommended by Hippocrates, be reduced in fevers and in some other illnesses.

Public baths, such as those at Bath and Buxton, had regained some of the popularity they had enjoyed before the epidemic of syphilis in the sixteenth century. Patients were encouraged not only to bathe in the saline water but also to drink it. Mineral springs were free to all but spas were established for the wealthy, who suffered most from gout and stone.[56]

Sydenham believed that failure to take regular exercise not only promoted gout but also predisposed to the development of kidney stone. The exercise he recommended was riding on horseback or, failing that, in a coach. The patient with gout should do this unless 'the pain is so violent that he cannot bear Motion'.[57] The only effective pain-killer Sydenham knew was laudanum (opium).

Sydenham's treatment of smallpox and of scarlet fever was much simpler than the conventional treatment of the time and than his own elaborate treatment of some other illnesses. He refused to confine a smallpox patient to bed before the fourth day of the illness and refused to heat the room, load him with blankets, and administer hot drinks. He claimed better results than were obtained with the fashionable 'warm' treatment.[58]

During epidemics of plague in a city Hippocrates had advised early flight and late return, although he pointed out that some must stay to care for the sick. Contact with patients should be avoided and protective measures taken. This advice was followed during the epidemics of plague in the seventeenth century (Chapter 10).

A particular case, the royal touch for the king's evil (p. 150), reached its peak of popularity in the seventeenth century, so much so that Charles II demanded a medical certificate to prove the need for it. Patients seeking the royal touch from William III were sent away by him with the words: 'God give you better health and more sense'.[59] The king's evil is scrofula (tuberculosis of the lymph glands of the neck).

Paediatrics

In the seventeenth century physicians normally treated children as well as adults, though some quacks claimed to be specialists in diseases of children. The most influential books on the subject were the sixteenth-century *Boke of Chyldren* (p. 49), François Mauriceau's *Observations sur la grossesse et l'accouchement*, and, at the end of the century, *De morbis acutis infantum* (1689) by Walter Harris, translated into German in 1691, English in 1693, and French in 1730, and very widely used.

Infants were wrapped in swaddling clothes, which restricted their movements but were believed to prevent deformities occurring while the bones were still soft. It was fashionable for the children of the wealthy to be suckled by a wet-nurse but the milk of cows or other animals was not used for fear that it would convey undesirable animal properties to the child. Weaning was often delayed until the first dentition was complete, though Pechey advised earlier weaning, starting with honey or oil of almonds.[60]

Diseases listed in the 1628 London Bills of Mortality as fatal to children include thrush, smallpox, measles, teething, worms, scurvy and swine-pox (chickenpox).[61] Infancy itself was listed as a cause of death (chrisomes = infants). Children also died of adult diseases, especially plague. Diphtheria, whooping cough, and mumps were common (Chapter 10). Congenital syphilis and scurvy were known but were often confused.

Walter Harris

Most children's diseases, according to Walter Harris, a distinguished Fellow of the College of Physicians, are due to excess of acid. Excess acid in the stomach, he believed, causes nausea, vomiting, and eructations.[62] Purging was necessary to get rid of the acid and safe drugs to be administered included crab's eyes, oyster shells, egg-shells, chalk, coral, pearls, bezoar, burnt hartshorn and burnt ivory. At least some of these are predominantly alkaline and would counteract acidity. Crab's eyes were considered useful also in the treatment of fever, and a purge, such as rhubarb or senna, might be given. Blood-letting was not recommended for young children, except in the treatment of convulsions, and Harris thought infants with smallpox or measles might be better off untreated. He disapproved of opiates and cordials for children.[63]

Robert Pemell

A country physician, Robert Pemell, noted that convulsions are common in the new-born; he treated them with a julep of 'Piony [peony] water and Linden water, syrope of Piony, spirit of black Cherries and magister of Coral'.[64] Between fits he gave the infant a purgative and hung round its neck a root of peony or white bryony. To eliminate worms he administered wormseed and moss, with roots of dittany and tormentil, all powdered and given in 'any convenient liquor'. To relieve the pain of teething 'the gums were anointed with the braynes of an hare myxte with capons grece and honey'.[65] If this failed it might be necessary to cut the gums.

John Pechey

The last seventeenth-century book on paediatrics was John Pechey's *General Treatise of the Diseases of Infants and Children* (1697). In it he describes the common ailments of children, including skin diseases, and recommends appropriate treatment for each. Unlike many of his contemporaries, he advised that children should not be bled or given strong purges, except for rickets, for which his treatment included purging and sometimes blood-letting as well as herbal remedies.[66]

Psychiatry

Psychiatry, like paediatrics, was not considered a specialty in the seventeenth century; medical textbooks describe the symptoms, signs, and treatment of mental as well as physical disorders. Bruel (p. 50) dealt with melancholy, lethargy, and mania as well as headache, apoplexy, vertigo and paralysis. Willis added delirium and, oddly, included gout in his book on nervous disorders, *Two Discourses Concerning the Soul of Brutes* (1672).[67] In effect the only forms of lunacy generally recognised were melancholy and mania, although Willis had written in 1650 the earliest description of manic-depressive psychosis.[68] Philip Barrough described the wild behaviour of mania, which he distinguished from frenzy, which was accompanied by fever.[69] The commonest signs of melancholy were 'fearfulnesse, sadnesse, hatred, and . . . strange imaginations'.[70]

Sydenham distinguished hysteria from madness and described the wide range of symptoms of hysteria, the commonest of which he found to be pain in the back.[71] He considered it to be due to imbalance of animal spirits and treated it with the usual bleeding, purging, and medicines which 'fortified the blood'. Hysteria was inevitably a disease of women because it was traditionally attributed to disorder or displacement of the womb (Greek, hystera = uterus); the similar, but less common, disorder in men was called hypochondria.

Melancholy was a frequent and fashionable complaint of aristocrats and gentlefolk. A labourer or his wife could not aspire to this distinction but could be 'mopish'. More severe insanity might be violent or non-violent lunacy, the signs of which included inability to recognise relations or friends, or the performance of senselessly destructive acts; typically madmen tore their clothes.[72]

Mad men and women were usually looked after in the family or by friends. Until the middle of the seventeenth century Bethlehem (Bedlam) Hospital in London was the only lunatic asylum in the country but some private institutions were established later in the century.[73] The property of a lunatic was effectively safeguarded by the law and returned to him if he recovered; if impoverished he and his dependent family were to be maintained by the parish as 'deserving poor'.

The treatment of the mentally, as of the physically, ill was primarily blood-letting, purges, and enemas, supplemented by various medicaments. The concept of insanity as possession by a devil led to the practice of exorcism, which was losing popularity by the end of the century.

The two most prolific seventeenth-century writers on mental disorders, Robert Burton and Richard Napier, were both clergymen, not trained in medicine.

Robert Burton

Robert Burton was an Oxford scholar, whose extraordinarily comprehensive *Anatomy of Melancholy* (1621) was based on very wide knowledge of the literature, with no practical experience. He regarded depression (melancholy) as the commonest mental disorder: it was particularly prevalent among the gentry since 'there is no greater cause of melancholy than idleness.'[74] Idleness predisposes to love, which predisposes to melancholy, which cannot be cured by medicine. Mirth and merry company are the best remedies. Burton thought that religious melancholy, often associated with excessive fasting, solitude and meditation, was promoted by ministers preaching damnation and might lead to madness.[75]

Richard Napier

Richard Napier, although an ordained clergyman without medical qualifications (p. 138), spent most of his working life treating mentally and physically ill patients. His records, which have been analyzed by Michael MacDonald, include 2039 cases of mental disorder; of these 264 suspected that they had been bewitched and 148 were thought to be possessed by the Devil.[76] Most cases could be attributed to stress, most mental patients were women, and the commonest causes of stress were courtship and marriage. Less than 30 of Napier's mental patients were sufficiently ill to be considered lunatics by the local Courts of Wards, which were responsible for the support of indigent lunatics.[77]

Napier's treatment was essentially the same for the mentally as for the physically ill but, although psychological medicine was not at the time a known method of treatment, his sympathy and encouragement must have had a beneficial effect in many cases and many patients would be cured by their belief in the efficacy of the remedies applied.

CHAPTER 5

Medical Science

THERE WERE DRAMATIC DEVELOPMENTS in medical science in the seventeenth century, particularly in England, although the practice of medicine changed little in the course of the century. Some leading medical practitioners were also scientists, but their scientific discoveries had little influence on their practice. Nevertheless, the medical science of the Stuart period is the precursor of the scientific medicine of today. The Royal Society which received its royal charter from Charles II in 1662, gave scientists an opportunity to discuss and publish the results of their investigations.

Science, like medicine, has a very ancient history and, in its early days, was often confused with magic and superstition. Alchemy, the precursor of chemistry, was closely linked with magic. Its first practical functions were the extraction of metals from their ores and the preparation of dyes. Later its main object was to transmute other metals into gold and, in the field of medicine, to prepare 'potable gold', the *elixir vitae*, which would prolong not only life but also youthful vigour.[1] Secret formulae for this were still being claimed in the seventeenth century although alchemy was then being transformed into chemistry by the quantitative experimental work of Robert Boyle.[2]

Anatomy and botany were regarded as medical sciences from early times, anatomy because the physician or surgeon needed to know something of the structure of the body he was treating, and botany because most remedies were herbal and the physician had to be able to identify plants and know something of their medicinal properties. Other branches of science also made great advances in the seventeenth century. England led the field in physics and biology became an experimental science instead of merely descriptive botany and zoology. In the field of medicine the experimental study of bodily function (physiology) took the place of groundless speculation, there were some advances in embryology, and the science of vital statistics was born. Effective study of disease (pathology) dates from the eighteenth century and the study of the mode of action of drugs (pharmacology) only from the nineteenth.

Biology

Early and Renaissance biologists

Aristotle was concerned with the whole of human knowledge but his earliest and best writings were on plants and animals. His first-hand observations of animals were not surpassed for 2000 years.

Pedanius Dioscorides, a Greek surgeon in the Roman army in the first century AD, wrote a treatise on *Materia medica*, a description of plants and their uses in medicine which was regarded as the authoritative work on the subject for more than fifteen centuries.[3] Most medieval herbals were merely commentaries on it.

Botany, in the form of herbals for the identification of medicinal plants, developed and expanded during the Renaissance as explorers brought back from distant lands plants which had not been described by Dioscorides, among which were guaiac, introduced from America in 1508 and used in the treatment of syphilis, and sassafras, used to promote sweating. One of the first of the new botanists was Leonard Fuchs, a Bavarian, who published his *De historia stirpium*, based on original observations and with accurate woodcut illustrations, in 1546.

Kaspar Bauhin, professor of botany, anatomy, medicine, and Greek at Basel, published in 1596 *Pinax*, a compendium of botanical literature up to that time, which was the most influential textbook of botany since that of Dioscorides. He described about 6000 different plants and distinguished genera from species, thereby contributing to the binomial system of classification of plants and animals developed by Carl von Linné (Linnaeus) in the next century.[4] One of the best English herbals of the time is William Bullein's *Book of Simples* (1562) but the best known is John Gerarde's *Herball* (1597). In 1587 the College of Physicians had established a physic garden and appointed Gerard curator.[5]

Biology in the seventeenth century

The development and use of the microscope in the seventeenth century enabled biologists, such as Jan Swammerdam in Amsterdam, Marcello Malpighi in Bologna, and Antonj van Leeuwenhoek in Delft, to discover previously unknown living organisms and to describe the detailed structure of the organs of others. Swammerdam was the first to describe red blood corpuscles and the valves in lymph channels. Malpighi described the structure of plants in *Anatomia plantarum* (1675) and pointed out some common features of plant and animal life. He described the countless minute air-sacs (alveoli) at the end of the air passages in the lungs and the minute, tortuous blood vessels (capillaries), which convey blood from the smallest arteries to the smallest veins;[6] the last observation was the final evidence necessary to confirm William Harvey's theory of the circulation of the blood (p. 82). Malpighi was also the first to describe accurately the microscopic structure of liver, kidney and spleen. Van Leeuwenhoek made his own microscopes and was the first to describe spermatozoa and many micro-organisms. Robert Hooke at Oxford made accurate drawings of the microscopic structure of plants and animals, published in his *Micrographia* (1665). He described the cell wall of plant cells but the modern concept of a plant or animal cell dates from the nineteenth century.

John Ray, the leading English biologist of the seventeenth century, started to study botany in 1650 and zoology a few years later. After graduating BA and, later MA at Cambridge he travelled widely in England, Scotland, Wales and western Europe, collecting plants and making notes about animals. He met many of the leading scientists of Europe and became a Fellow of the Royal Society in 1667.[7] He published minor works, including a flora of Cambridge, before the first volume of his massive *Historia plantarum* (1686). He also wrote on birds, fishes, reptiles and insects. Ray was primarily concerned with identification and classification and his natural orders of plants are still acceptable in the twentieth century. His methods were modern, based on structural and physiological features instead of the legendary and magical elements which had influenced previous naturalists, but he still sought purpose in Nature, as expressed in his most popular book, *The Wisdom of God Manifested in the Works of the Creation* (1691).

Nehemiah Grew produced another important botanical work, his *Anatomy of Plants* (1682), based on their microscopic structure. Grew was a physician and a Fellow of the Royal Society who, like Ray, saw God's design in the structure of plants and animals. Other English biologists of the period were concerned with plants, mainly as sources of herbal medicines, and with animals, mainly for physiological research. John Pechey published in 1694 a herbal of 'such plants as grow in England and are not commonly known' (p. 63). Although this treatise is 'designed for general use' Pechey points out: 'it is very hazardous in many cases to administer physick without the advice of a physician'.[8]

Anatomy

Early anatomists

Herophilis of the Alexandrian school (p. 38) may have been the first to dissect the human body in public and record his observations.[9] He described the brain and its surrounding membranes, the liver, pancreas, and duodenum, the salivary glands, and the genital organs and he made the first clear distinction between arteries and veins.

Erasistratus, a younger contemporary of Herophilus, also performed public dissections and he described the nervous and circulatory systems in more detail than Herophilus. He tried to relate structure to function and is regarded by some as the founder of physiology. According to Celsus both Herophilus and Erasistratus performed some of their dissections on living criminals from the local prisons.[10]

Galen, about five centuries later, rescued the observations of Herophilus and Erasistratus from oblivion and published them along with others, including many of his own, in his numerous books on anatomy, which were unchallenged until the sixteenth century in spite of being inaccurate in some respects as human anatomy because many of his dissections were performed on the Barbary ape.[11] His description of bones, muscles and nerves was much in advance of all previous work, though his description of the heart and blood vessels was less satisfactory. Like Erasistratus, Galen tried to relate structure to function and he propounded an elaborate but false theory of the movement of the blood (p. 78). Unfortunately, Galen's views on anatomy and physiology were accepted as authoritative until the sixteenth century and some of them even in the seventeenth.

Middle Ages

After Galen there were no advances in anatomy for many centuries because neither the Christian church nor Islam permitted human dissection. At the University of Bologna, however, which had an important school of law, post-mortem examinations were permitted, especially in cases where death from poisoning was suspected. In the thirteenth century Mondino de'

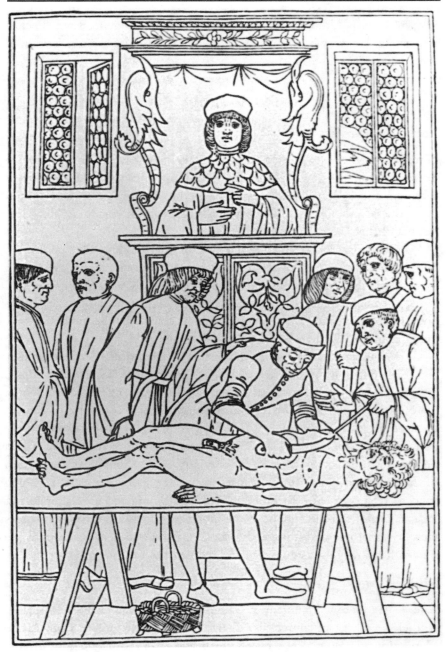

Figure 8. Mondino presiding at a dissection. From a 15th-century woodcut, reproduced in *A Short History of Medicine* by Charles Singer, 1928 (courtesy of Oxford University Press)

Luzzi performed public dissections there in spite of clerical and general hostility to the practice.[12] Although Mondino sometimes performed dissections himself the usual practice, then and later, was for the teacher to read aloud from a book while an assistant pointed to the parts he was describing (Fig 8).[13] The object of the exercise was not to seek new information but to demonstrate what had been described by Galen. Because of the opposition of the authorities few dissections were performed during the next two centuries, although some anatomists managed to obtain bodies for this purpose.

Renaissance and Reformation

In the fifteenth and sixteenth centuries human anatomy was studied by artists rather than by doctors. Donatello, Michelangelo, Raphael and Leonardo da Vinci all performed dissections and Leonardo's drawings of his own preparations are probably the first accurate representations of the parts of the human body. Physicians and surgeons preferred to accept the statements of classical writers rather than the evidence of their own eyes.

Andreas Vesalius, professor of surgery and anatomy at the University of Padua, introduced the modern pattern of anatomical teaching, based on observation rather than authority. His major work, *De humani corporis fabrica* (1543), based on direct observation and beautifully illustrated, is one of the greatest scientific textbooks of all time, although some of Galen's errors are still repeated in it.[14] The *Fabrica* comprises seven books, the first on bones and joints and succeeding volumes on muscles, blood vessels and nerves, abdominal viscera, heart and lungs and brain. At least twenty-five editions were published between 1543 and 1728 and they were widely copied.[15] Vesalius was succeeded at Padua by Matteo Realdo Colombo and he by Gabriele Falloppio (Fallopius), both distinguished anatomists, and Fallopius by Girolamo Fabrizi (Fabricius), one of whose students was the Englishman, William Harvey. Fabricius described and illustrated the valves in veins,[16] one of the clues which led Harvey to his discovery of the circulation of the blood (p. 82).

Anatomy in England

The study of anatomy in the English universities at the beginning of the seventeenth century still consisted of committing to memory the work of early anatomists, with very little direct observation of the parts of the human body, because of the reluctance of some professors of medicine to undertake dissection. Although the statutes of Oxford and Cambridge universities required the candidate for a licence to practise medicine or surgery or for a degree in medicine to 'witness anatomies' and a licence from Queen Elizabeth I granted Gonville and Caius College, Cambridge, the bodies of two executed felons each year for this purpose, the statutes were not strictly enforced.[17] As the century progressed, however, some important new contributions to anatomy were made by Englishmen. The first important treatise on anatomy by an English author, Helkiah Crooke's *Mikrokosmographia* (1615), followed the traditional pattern; it was compiled from the work of Bauhin and others with plates based on those of Vesalius. Advances in the science were due to those English anatomists who published their own observations: William Harvey at the College of Physicians, Thomas Willis and Richard Lower at Oxford and Francis Glisson at Cambridge.

William Harvey, the leading physiologist of the century, and physician to two kings (p. 12), was also a distinguished anatomist. In 1615 he was appointed Lumleian lecturer in anatomy at the College of Physicians, a post he held until a year before his death, though he could not perform his duties during the Civil Wars. The Lumleian lectureship, founded in 1581, was to be awarded to 'a Doctor of Physic of good practice and knowledge, who was to be paid an honest stipend, no less in amount than that received by the regius professors of law, divinity and physic in the universities of Oxford and Cambridge'.[18] The lectures were given twice a week throughout the year and the lecturer was to read for three-quarters of an hour in Latin and one-quarter in English, 'wherein that shall be plainly declared for those that understand not Latin'. Harvey's anatomy notes for these lectures have been edited, translated into English, and annotated by O'Malley *et al.* in 1961 and by Gweneth Whitteridge in 1964, quite an achievement because his handwriting is hard to read and the notes are in a mixture of English and Latin intended for his own use and not for publication.

Harvey first laid down his own rules for the lectures. The lecturer must first show his audience as much as he can of the body and should refer to clinical observations and to comparative anatomy. He should relate structure to function 'for the end of anatomy is knowledge of the part, why it exists, for what purpose it is necessary and what is its use'.[19] Harvey makes numerous references to observations by contemporary and by classical writers, especially Aristotle and Galen. Such is his deference to these authorities that, where his observations differ from those of Aristotle or Galen, he sometimes expresses the belief that a change in human anatomy must have occurred since the earlier observations, but he cannot accept Aristotle's statement that the heart has three ventricles or Galen's that there are pores in the septum of the heart, through which blood can pass from the right side to the left.

Thomas Willis, later a distinguished physician (p. 17), was appointed professor of natural philosophy at Oxford in 1660. He was a pioneer in the anatomy of the brain, his *Cerebri anatome* (1664), illustrated by Christopher Wren, being the first monograph on the brain and spinal cord to be published in England.[20] He described the arteries at the base of the brain (circle of Willis), the eleventh cranial (spinal accessory) nerves, and the cerebellum and its peduncles and he had some concept of localisation of function in the brain. Willis was fortunate in being assisted by Richard Lower, a distinguished anatomist in his own right and author of an important monograph on the heart, in which William Harvey's work is acknowledged. Lower described the anatomy of the heart in detail, noting the oblique course of the muscle fibres and the effect of this on the change of shape during contraction.[21] He also noted, from his study of the base of the skull, that catarrh could not pass from the brain to the nostrils,[22] which was the current belief. When Willis and Lower moved to London to practise medicine, anatomy at Oxford reverted to its earlier torpor.

Francis Glisson who became regius professor of physic at Cambridge in 1636, did his most important anatomical work before this as lecturer in anatomy at the College of Physicians.[23] His *Anatomia hepatis* (1654) was the first major monograph on liver structure and remained the authoritative work on this for he next century. Like his contemporaries, Willis and Lower at Oxford, Glisson left Cambridge to become a distinguished London physician; he was elected President of the College of Physicians in 1667.

Thomas Wharton, a contemporary of Glisson at Cambridge, investigated the anatomy of glands and described the duct of the submaxillary gland in the mouth, previously described by Galen and by Avicenna but now known as Wharton's duct.[24]

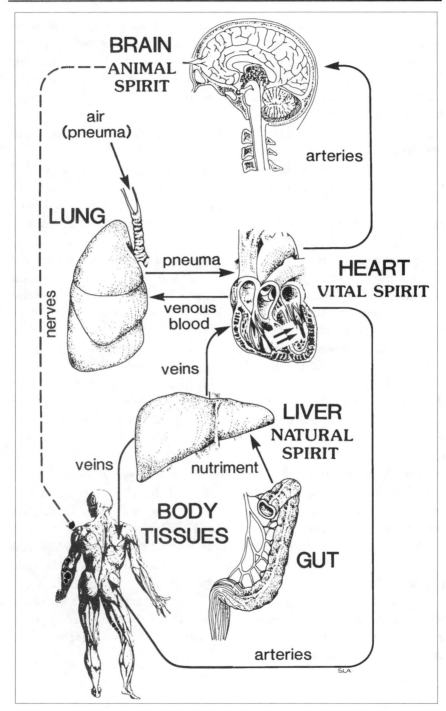

BRAIN
ANIMAL SPIRIT

air (pneuma)

LUNG

nerves

arteries

pneuma

HEART
VITAL SPIRIT

venous blood

veins

LIVER
NATURAL SPIRIT

veins

nutriment

BODY TISSUES

GUT

arteries

SLA

Physiology

Before the seventeenth century there was no science of physiology, though speculation about body function was rife from the time of the ancient Greeks, as in the concepts of temperaments and humours. Erasistratus (p. 73) believed that arteries contain not blood but only 'vital spirit', formed in the left side of the heart from air taken in by the lungs, carried to the heart in the pulmonary veins, and distributed in the arteries throughout the body. The nerves were thought to be hollow and to contain 'animal spirit' which was formed in the brain and passed into the nerves.[25] The theory that contraction of muscle is due to animal spirit pumped into it from the nerve was still accepted until the seventeenth century.

Galen

Galen believed that the blood is formed by the liver from nutriment absorbed from the gut (Fig. 9). It flows from the liver in the veins to all parts of the body, the flow to the lungs passing through the right side of the heart. It carries another spirit, additional to the two described by Erasistratus, the 'natural spirit', formed in the liver and essential to life.[26] The function of the arteries, as described by Galen, is more complicated; air passes backwards and forwards between the lungs and the left side of the heart, where it mixes with some blood, which has passed through invisible channels from the right side to produce the vital spirit described by Erasistratus.[27] The blood is warmed by the heart and distributed from there in the arteries throughout the body, so blood reaches the tissues in both arteries and veins. According to Galen the vital spirit, which reaches the brain, is transformed into the animal spirit described by Erasistratus, which passes down the nerves to the various organs. Galen's views were still widely accepted at the beginning of the seventeenth century, though Vesalius had been unable to find the channels with Galen believed traversed the septum of the heart (p. 77) and Miguel Servetus, in 1553, had described the passage of blood from pulmonary arteries to pulmonary veins through the lungs, where it mixed with air and became red.

Opposite: Figure 9. Galen's concept of the passage of blood and nerve fluid (interpreted by Dr. Peter Brain and drawn by Susan Abraham, Medical Graphics, Groote Schuur Hospital)

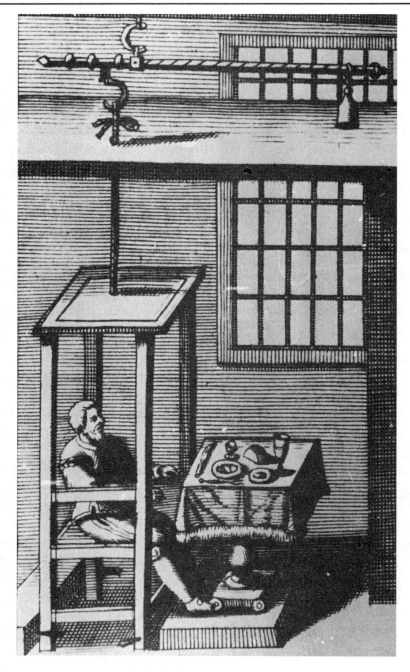

Figure 10. Sanctorius in his balance. From *Medicina Statica* by Sanctorius (courtesy of the Wellcome Historical Medical Library, London)

European physiology in the seventeenth century

Spectacular advances took place in the science of physiology in the seventeenth century. Santorio Santorio (Sanctorius) of Padua applied mechanics to human physiology in *De medicina statica* (1614). He devised a balance to weigh himself (Fig. 10) and found that he lost weight progressively between meals, possibly the first study of metabolism.[28] He also measured body temperature with a simple thermometer and pulse rate from the length of a pendulum which swung synchronously with the pulse.[29] In *Elementorum myologia specimen* (1667), Niels Stensen, a Dane, described the microscopic structure of muscle fibres and observed that they contract when stimulated.[30] Giovanni Alfonso Borelli, an Italian mathematician, applied physical principles to the mechanics of muscular contraction in *De motu animalium* (1681), and has been claimed as the founder of the iatrophysical school, which seeks to explain body function in terms of physics, though he was not the first to do so. He rejected the idea that muscle contraction is due to a fluid pumped into it from the nerve; although he still believed, wrongly, that muscle increases in volume when it contracts. He thought that this was due to a kind of fermentation taking place in the muscle when stimulated. He accepted Harvey's views on the circulation of the blood and realised that it was the elasticity of the arteries that maintains the flow of blood between heart beats.

The idea that physiological processes can be explained in terms of chemistry, promoted by Paracelsus in the sixteenth century (p. 44), was advanced again by the Belgian mystic, Jean Baptiste van Helmont, who recognised the physiological importance of ferments (now called enzymes) in the processes of digestion.[31] He discovered that a gas (*gas sylvestre*), which we now call carbon dioxide (CO_2), is produced in the process of fermentation of wine[32] but he failed to appreciate its significance in respiration or to distinguish it from the poisonous carbon monoxide (CO). Van Helmont has been claimed as the founder of the iatrochemical school, which explains biological functions in terms of chemistry, but his writings were published only posthumously in 1648 and Paracelsus has a stronger claim.

The importance of chemistry in physiology was appreciated also by François de la Boë (Sylvius), who created at Leyden the first chemical laboratory in any university. He regarded digestion as a process of fermentation and recognised the importance of saliva and of gastric and pancreatic juice in promoting this.[33] He was also a competent anatomist, whose name is commemorated in the fissure of Sylvius in the brain, and the first European professor of medicine outside Padua to provide clinical teaching.

Physiology in England

William Harvey (p. 12) is widely regarded as the founder of modern physiology and, in the words of Sir Charles Dodds: 'It is justifiable to say that Harvey's discovery of the circulation of blood formed the foundation of modern medicine.'[34] His claim to fame, however, lies not so much in his discovery as in how it was achieved. Having come to the conclusion that the blood must circulate round the body Harvey proceeded to test his hypothesis by experiment and provided quantitative evidence for it by ingenious experiments and analysis of numerical data.

In 1628 Harvey published *Exercitatio anatomica de motu cordis et sanguinis in animalibus*, usually referred to as *De motu cordis*. The book has been translated into English on several occasions, notably by Robert Willis in 1847, by Kenneth Franklin in 1957, and by Gweneth Whitteridge in 1976. In his dedication of the book to the president and Fellows of the College of Physicians Harvey explains why he has written it.

> On several earlier occasions in my anatomical lectures I revealed my new concept of the heart's movement and function and of the blood's passage round the body. Having now, however, for more than nine years confirmed it in your presence by numerous ocular demonstrations and having freed it from the objections of learned and skilful anatomists I have yielded to the repeated desire of all, and the pressing request of some, and in this small book have published it for all to see.[35]

Harvey was fully aware of the opposition which a new idea, such as this, would encounter. 'But what remains to be said is so novel and unheard of character that I not only fear injury to myself from the envy of a few, but I tremble lest I have mankind at large for my enemies.[36]

In *De motu cordis* Harvey first described in detail the observations and experiments on which his hypothesis of the circulation of the blood was based. He noted that contraction of the heart is followed immediately by expansion of the arteries as blood is forced into them and that blood flows more forcibly from an artery when it is cut at this time. The valves in the heart ensure that blood passes only in one direction through the heart, from veins to arteries. He calculated the amount of blood which must pass

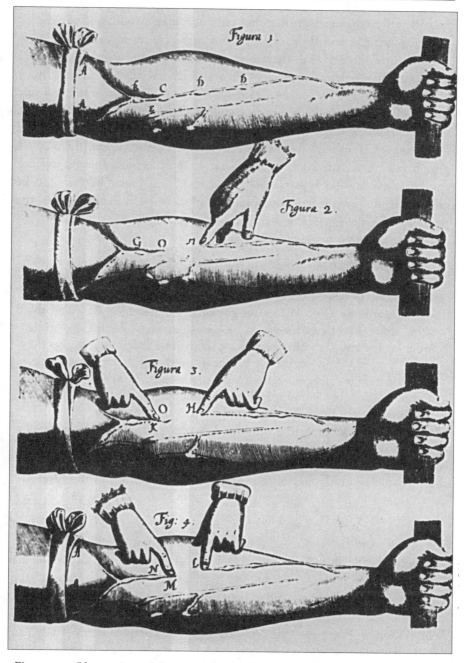

Figure 11. Obstruction of forearm veins to show valves. From *De motu cordis* by William Harvey (courtesy of the Hunterian Library, University of Glasgow)

into the arteries; even assuming that only one drachm of blood is expelled from the heart at each beat, in one hour there are more than 1000 beats, expelling more blood than there is in the whole body.[37] Cutting the neck arteries of an ox drains it of blood in less than one-quarter of an hour.

The arteries above a tight ligature round the arm are distended and pulsate, while the hand becomes swollen and deeply coloured and the veins prominent; when the ligature is released the swelling subsides and the veins collapse. Obstruction of individual veins makes them swell peripherally to the obstruction. Blood can be pushed with a finger towards the heart but not back past a valve (Fig 11). A segment of vein can be emptied if the flow from the periphery is blocked but fills again when the peripheral block is released.

Having outlined his evidence, Harvey stated his conclusions.

> Since all things, both argument and ocular demonstration, show that blood passes through the lungs and heart by the action of the ventricles and is sent for distribution to all parts of the body, where it makes its way into the veins and pores of the flesh, and then flows by the veins from the circumference on every side to the centre, from the lesser to the greater veins, and is by them finally discharged into the vena cava and right auricle of the heart, and this in such a quantity or in such a flux and reflux thither by the arteries, hither by the veins, as cannot possibly be supplied by the ingesta, and is much greater than can be required for mere purposes of nutrition; it is absolutely necessary to conclude that the blood in the animal body is impelled in a circle and is in a state of ceaseless motion; that this is the act or function which the heart performs by means of its pulse; and that it is the sole and only end of the motion and contraction of the heart.[38]

Harvey's scheme is as we know it today. The missing element, the capillaries, can only be seen with a microscope, which Harvey did not use. They were first described four years after Harvey's death by Marcello Malpighi (p. 72); this observation filled the gap in Harvey's model of the human circulation. As Harvey had anticipated, his novel idea of the circulation of the blood excited violent opposition from traditional galenists, including Pierre Gassendi at the Hague, Caspar Hofman at Altdorf and Jean Riolan at Paris. He was supported by Franciscus Sylvius of Leyden, Sir Kenelm Digby, Francis Glisson and Robert Fludd in England, and, with reservations, by René Descartes in Holland.

Thomas Willis at Oxford not only described the anatomy of the arteries at the base of the brain, now known as the circle of Willis (p. 77), but showed experimentally that this is a safety device, maintaining the blood supply to the brain if one of the arteries is obstructed.[39] Some of his views on localisation of function in the nervous system were sound but he went astray in believing that muscle contraction involves an explosion due to nerve juice and blood meeting in the muscle.

Richard Lower, who assisted Thomas Willis in some of his anatomical work (p. 77), was the first exponent of blood transfusion. In 1665 he transfused blood from one dog into another and later, without ill effects, he transfused some ounces of blood from a sheep into a man.[40] Like Servetus in the previous century (p. 79) he noticed the change in colour of blood as it passed through the lungs.

> This must be attributed entirely to the lungs, as I have found that the blood, which enters the lungs completely venous and dark in colour, returns from them quite arterial and bright. For, if the anterior part of the chest is cut away and the lungs are continuously insufflated by a pair of bellows inserted into the trachea, and they are also pricked with a needle in various places to allow free passage of air through them then, on the pulmonary vein being cut near the left auricle, the blood will flow out into a suitably placed receptacle completely bright-red in colour . . . Further that this red colour is entirely due to the penetration of air into the blood is quite clear from the fact that, while the blood becomes red throughout its mass in the lungs (because the air diffuses in them through all the particles of blood, and hence becomes thoroughly mixed with the blood) when venous blood is received into a vessel, the surface and upper part of it takes on this scarlet colour through exposure to the air.[41]

John Mayow, also at Oxford, in his *Tractatus quinque medico-physici* (1674), demonstrated that the dark venous blood becomes bright red in the lungs by taking up an ingredient of air, which is also a constituent of nitre (KNO_3);[42] he called it 'nitro-aerial spirit' and it is now called oxygen. He also described the mechanism of breathing, noting that inspiration is caused by contraction of the intercostal muscles, raising the ribs, and by contraction of the diaphragm, both movements increasing the volume of the chest cavity so that air under atmospheric pressure enters the lungs. He found that expiration is due to relaxation of these muscles.[43] He also stated, correctly, that animal heat is produced mainly in the skeletal muscles and not in the heart as was previously believed.[44]

Francis Glisson (p. 16) developed the concept of irritability (appropriate response to stimulation) of living matter in *Tractatus de natura energetica* (1672), and also demonstrated that the muscles of the arm decrease in volume when they contract.[45] This disproved the view expressed by William Croone in his 'little treatise', *De ratione motus musculorum* (1664) and later by Borelli in Italy (p. 81) that contracting muscle increases in volume as a result of some sort of fermentation or effervescence set up by stimulation.

Robert Boyle, in *A Continuation of New Experiments Physico-Mechanical* (1682), concluded that the essential function of respiration is to ventilate the blood as it passes through the lungs, that waste products are eliminated in the expired air, and that some portion of the air is essential to life.[46] His colleague, Robert Hooke, demonstrated to the Royal Society that aeration of the lungs rather than movement is essential; when, like Lower, he punctured the lungs of a dog in several places and pumped air through them from the trachea, the heart continued to beat as long as the lungs were aerated.[47] He found that part of the air (the part we now call oxygen) is essential for plant or animal life.

Embryology

Early embryology

Aristotle studied the development of the chick embryo from day to day, noting the sequence of development of the different organs.[48] He believed that the mammalian embryo develops not from an egg but from a combination of male and female semen. Since neither the mammalian ovum nor the spermatozoon was visible to the naked eye, subsequent writers agreed with this theory of generation but they differed on the sequence of development of organs in the embryo; Galen thought the liver was the first to appear, followed by the heart and then the brain, Avicenna thought the umbilicus came first, and Fabricius the skeleton.[49]

Embryology in the seventeenth century

Embryology at the beginning of the seventeenth century was still essentially that of Aristotle and Galen. The two embryological treatises of Fabricius of Aquapendente (p. 75), *De formato foetu* (1600) and *De formatione ovi et pulli* (published posthumously in 1621), repeated Galen's observations in more detail but the embryonic membranes were correctly defined[50] and

De formato foetu was illustrated with thirty-three plates. He believed that animal embryos may develop from an egg or from seminal fluid or spontaneously, a view still held by many even after it was rejected by William Harvey.

Later in the century Marcello Malpighi put embryology on a firmer basis by using a microscope to study the early stages of development but, unfortunately, claimed that he could see the principal parts of a chicken in an unincubated egg.[51] This statement, supporting the claim of the English physician, Nathaniel Highmore, that the animal is preformed in the fertilized egg,[52] was expressed in 1672 in a letter to the Royal Society and set embryology on the wrong track for many years.

English embryology

William Harvey, the greatest English embryologist as well as the leading physiologist of the century, published his embryological observations in 1651 under the title of *Exercitationes de generatione animalium*. The whole book was translated by an unknown author in 1653, by Robert Willis in 1847, and by Gweneth Whitteridge in 1981. The material for this work had been collected during the greater part of Harvey's long life; there are references to embryology in his anatomical lectures and in *De motu cordis*. The animals whose development was studied in most detail, presumably because he had access to the material, are the chicken and the deer, but many others are mentioned including man; in *De generatione* he refers to seventy-one different species.[53] 'Nature certainly is a most reliable interpreter of her own secrets', he wrote, 'and the things she shows more sparingly or more obscurely in one kind of animal she explains more clearly and more openly in another one.'[54] The observations are less valuable than they would have been if Harvey had used a microscope and the deer was an unfortunate choice for the study of embryology because of the long latent period between insemination and the appearance of a visible embryo; nevertheless he concluded that the embryo is not preformed in the egg and 'its parts are not fashioned simultaneously but emerge in their due succession and order'.[55] Perhaps the most important observations in this book are not on embryology but on scientific method. In a long philosophical introduction Harvey discusses Aristotle's and Galen's opinions on generation and mentions subsequent observations, notably by Fabricius. He stresses the importance of confirming traditional views by the evidence of one's own senses. Some universal principles emerge from his own work, the most important being that 'all mammals are in some sort born from eggs'.[56] Harvey did not exclude spontaneous generation of some other animals, a concept which was disproved only by Louis Pasteur in the nineteenth century, and he never grasped the basic principle of fertilisation of the ovum by the spermatozoon, presumably because in mammals he could see neither. 'All Animals whatsoever', he says, 'which arise from Male and Female are generated by the coition of both Sexes and so begotten as it were . . . by a kind of contagion'.[57] Although Harvey's observations were always sound, his interpretation of them in terms of the knowledge of the time sometimes led him into gross error.

Some other Englishmen, in addition to Nathaniel Highmore (p. 87), made embryological observations in the seventeenth century. Sir Kenelm Digby, in *The Nature of Bodies* (1664), described personal observations on the chick embryo, whose development he attributed to 'inexplicable forces'. Walter Charleton believed that a 'formative agent' transforms the initially homogeneous material into the diverse organs of the embryo and Sir Thomas Browne (p. 31) believed that this agent is God. Robert Boyle (p. 86) showed that egg white is of similar chemical nature to some parts of the body and assumed that it is 'absumed and contexted or contrived into the body of the chick and its several parts.'[58]

Vital Statistics

A branch of medical science which may fairly be said to have started in England in the seventeenth century is vital statistics. England had been more fortunate than most European countries in preserving official records because it was not ravaged by internal strife during the sixteenth century, and even the Civil Wars of the seventeenth century caused only limited local destruction of records.

John Graunt

The originator of this new branch of medical science was a London tradesman, John Graunt, whose book, *Natural and Political Observations upon the Bills of Mortality of London* (1662), was the first step in the application of mathematics to official records and gained him Fellowship of the Royal Society. From 1538 each parish in England had been required to keep a register of christenings, marriages, and burials and these records were consolidated in an annual report for the diocese.[59] Bills of Mortality were no longer published after the epidemic of plague in 1595 but when another epidemic started in 1603 (p. 153) some parishes started to publish them again. During the next major epidemic of plague in 1625 the Company of Parish Clerks obtained a decree to prepare and print the Bills of Mortality for London parishes and liberties.[60]

The earlier records merely distinguished plague from other causes of death but, from 1629, the other causes were specified. Graunt noted that 'Consumption and cough', 'Chrisomes [neonates] and Infants' and 'Ague and fever' all ranked above plague as causes of death in the twenty years before 1661.[61] More than one-third of all deaths were of children under the age of 6 years. Graunt was aware that the figures were unreliable because they were based on reports by unskilled and often corrupt 'searchers', who examined the bodies.[62] Lunacy and syphilis were seldom recorded because these ailments were not respectable and searchers might be bribed not to report cases of plague so that the rest of the family would not be confined to the house (p. 155), but figures for other easily identifiable diseases and for accidents were probably reliable. Births were under-recorded because not all infants were christened and not all christenings were registered.[63]

William Petty

The science of vital statistics was further developed by William Petty, a man of many parts. After studying at Caen, Leyden, Utrecht, Amsterdam and Paris he incorporated as Doctor of Medicine at Oxford in 1650. The same year he was appointed Professor of Music at Gresham College. He was appointed Physician to the Army in Ireland in 1652 and knighted in 1661. He was an early Fellow of the Royal Society and the author of numerous essays and books, including *Observations on the Dublin Bills of Mortality* (1681) and *Essays on Political Arithmetic* (1687), two early classics in the history of vital statistics. Petty attempted quantitative assessment of trade, manufacture, revenue and other topics as well as population and health and he urged the establishment of hospitals and the provision of adequate medical care for the community.[64]

Gregory King

The last English exponent of political arithmetic in the seventeenth century was Gregory King, described at the time as a herald, accountant, surveyor and mathematician.[65] The manuscript of his *Natural and Politicall Observations* attracted much attention and was widely quoted before it first appeared in print in 1802. King analysed the population and health of the country but his indications as to source materials are vague and, when he states them, of doubtful validity. His population figures were derived from hearth tax returns and an estimate of the number of people per house but he admitted that 'What ye true Number of ye People of England may be, is not only uncertain but very difficult to compute; by reason of the great neglects and omissions in all the Publick Registers and Assessments.'[66]

The future of vital statistics

By the end of the century health statistics were available not only for England but also for some other European countries and for the new American colonies. Administrators showed more interest than physicians in this new field of information. Most physicians, like Thomas Sydenham (p. 22), were more concerned with observation and description of the individual patient and his illness than with the analysis of large numbers of cases, but vital statistics made possible the study of public health and the development of preventive medicine, which would eventually save more lives than successful treatment of individual patients.

CHAPTER 6

The Apothecary

B Y THE BEGINNING OF THE SEVENTEENTH CENTURY the English apothecary had an established place in society and a less clearly defined position in the medical hierarchy. Although their official duty was only to prepare and sell drugs prescribed by a physician, many apothecaries also examined and treated patients. From the prolonged conflict with the physicians over their right to do this the apothecaries emerged victorious in 1703 (p. 6). As apothecaries devoted more time and attention to medical practice their medicines might be supplied by druggists. Such specialists in the preparation of medicines had existed from ancient times.

Early Pharmacy

The earliest medical records include prescriptions of drugs (p. 35). Although many physicians would collect and prepare their own remedies even ancient Egypt had druggists who specialised in preparing drugs for physicians. The practice continued in ancient Greece and in the Roman empire, although Galen taught that physicians should prepare their own medicines.[1] Two complex mixtures of herbal and animal constituents, theriac and mithridatium (p. 39), recommended by Galen and still popular in the seventeenth century, were primarily intended as antidotes to a variety of venoms and poisons, but came to be prescribed as a panacea for illnesses, including plague.[2]

Most developments in pharmacy, as in medicine, during the Middle Ages, were due to the Arabs. The physicians, Rhazes, (p. 41) and Avicenna (p. 41) and others, described drugs and their preparation, including drugs from Persia and India, previously unknown in western Europe; these included camphor, cassia, cloves, senna and tamarind.[3] The division of labour between pharmacy and medicine became more pronounced. Arab pharmacy was introduced into Europe in the *Antidotarium* of Salerno (twelfth century), summaries of which were used as late as the eighteenth century.

In England, until the twelfth century, no distinction was made between physician, surgeon or druggist.[4] The Saxon leech performed all these functions, as did the monks who were responsible for most medical care under the Normans. In the sixteenth century, when Henry VIII abolished the monasteries, some monks became apothecaries.[5]

The English apothecary

In the thirteenth century some spicers, who specialised in selling medicines, were called apothecaries. In the fourteenth century pepperers, spicers and apothecaries formed the Grocers' Company in London. In other towns there were mixed guilds of barbers, surgeons and apothecaries; in Norwich the Company of Physicians and Barber-Surgeons admitted apothecaries to membership.[6] In York they were incorporated in the Merchant Adventurers' Company, which included grocers, mercers and ironmongers; in Canterbury they were associated with grocers, chandlers and fishmongers, and in Coventry many apothecaries were members of the Mercers' Company.[7] Restrictive regulations on trade in towns made it important to belong to a guild but, except in London, the apothecaries were not strong enough to form their own guild and, even in London, this did not happen until 1617. An apothecary's shop usually comprised a front room for sales and a back room for preparations. The front room would often display a stuffed alligator or crocodile and jars of medicines, decorated and labelled. The large glass containers of red and green fluid, which graced the window of many a chemist and druggist early in the twentieth century, date from the apothecary's shop of some centuries ago.

At the beginning of the sixteenth century there was no official regulation of medical practice in England. An apothecary was free to assist a physician or to practise medicine himself. The assistance might include venesection, drawing teeth, or the administration of an enema, although it was more usual for these tasks to be performed by a surgeon. By an Act of 1511 all medical practitioners in or near London were required to be examined on their fitness to practise and to be registered, but apothecaries as well as physicians were eligible for the licence to practise. Although the College of Physicians, from its foundation in 1518, tried to gain absolute control of medical practice in London, and later throughout the country, it was unable to do so.

By an Act of 1540 the Censors of the College of Physicians were authorised to 'search, view and see the apothecary wares, drugs and stuffs',[8] an authority which they exercised for three centuries and which was very necessary prior to the foundation of the Society of Apothecaries in 1617 because many of the apothecaries' herbs and spices were in poor condition and many apothecaries did not stock the ingredients of the prescriptions they were supposed to make up. From the foundation of the Society it was usually the apothecaries who undertook this task, although the physicians had the right to do it and a physician might join the representatives of the apothecaries in their inspection. The premises not only of registered apothecaries, but of anyone offering medicines for sale, could be inspected and the vendor fined if his goods were faulty. When unsatisfactory goods were found they were usually burnt in front of the door of the shop.

Since there were not enough physicians for the country's needs an Act of 1543 allowed 'every person being the King's subject having knowledge of the nature of herbs, roots and waters . . . within any part of the realm of England . . . to practice, use and minister any herb or herbs . . . according to their cunning, experience and knowledge'.[9]

The Society of Apothecaries

By a Charter of 1606 the London apothecaries were formally united with the grocers but, by a later Charter in 1617, they became independent as a separate guild, 'The Master, Wardens and Society of the Art and Mystery of the Apothecaries of the City of London'.[10] The apothecaries were a society, later a 'Worshipful Society', whereas the grocers were a company, the distinction between an art and a trade. From its formation until the creation of the General Medical Council in 1858, according to Sir Zachary Cope, 'the Apothecaries' Society had the chief formative influence on the medical profession in England and Wales'.[11]

It was the physicians of King James I, Theodore de Mayerne (p. 19) and Henry Atkins, who persuaded him to grant a Royal Charter to the Society of Apothecaries. Separation from the grocers was opposed by the Grocers' Company and by some apothecaries, who feared loss of income, but the objections were over-ruled by the King. The first Master, Edmond Phillips, the first Wardens, Stephen Higgins and Thomas Townes, and the first twenty-one Assistants were named in the Charter[12] but the new Society had difficulty in attracting members. Admission demanded a seven-year apprenticeship and examination by apothecaries and physicians. Then there was a fee of £20 to be paid, a silver spoon to be presented to the Society, and an oath 'well and faithfully to execute their said offices', which some were unwilling to take.[13] Probably under pressure from the grocers the Lord Mayor of London asked the King in 1624 to repeal the Apothecaries' Charter, which he refused to do.[14]

The Society's first duties were inspecting drugs, sometimes in collaboration with the College of Physicians (p.93) and settling disputes between masters and apprentices. No member was allowed to sue another member without the Society's permission. A royal proclamation in 1620 forbade the compounding of medicines in London and within seven miles of the city without supervision by the apothecaries.[15]

About 1620 the Society applied for and was granted a coat of arms (Fig. 12). This depicts Apollo, the god of healing, vanquishing the dragon

Figure 12. Arms of the Worshipful Society of Apothecaries of London

of disease. The crest is a rhinoceros, whose powdered horn was greatly valued as a drug and still commands high prices in some Eastern countries today for its supposedly aphrodisiac qualities. The supporters are unicorns, fabulous beasts, whose horn was reputed to have healing properties. The motto may be translated: 'I am spoken of throughout the world as one who brings help'.[16] In 1630 members of the Society were granted by the City of London the right to wear a special livery on ceremonial occasions and to vote for Aldermen and Lord Mayor. The Assistants were required to wear their gowns at formal meetings.

In 1632 the Society bought property in Blackfriars, including a hall for its meetings, a laboratory for compounding galenic medicines, and some adjacent houses, which were let. The hall was badly damaged in the Great Fire of 1666 but rebuilt shortly thereafter, and in 1672 a chemical laboratory was established in the new building; in both these laboratories medicines were prepared for sale.[17] In 1702 the Society was awarded a lucrative contract to equip the surgeons' medical chests for the navy.[18] In 1673 a 'physic garden' was rented in Chelsea for growing some of the rare herbs and for teaching botany to apprentice apothecaries. John Watts, appointed superintendent of the garden in 1680, had a greenhouse constructed and introduced so many rare plants that the garden became famous throughout Europe. He and his successors spent so much on the garden that it was a financial burden to the Society until it was purchased, reorganised, and presented to the Society in 1722 by Sir Hans Sloane.[19] 'Herbarizing expeditions' were also organised to suitable country districts near London; on these expeditions apprentices were taught to recognise 'simples' (individual herbs).

As Copeman has pointed out, the Society of Apothecaries is unique as a craft guild whose craft has developed from a trade into a learned profession.[20] Today it continues to license medical practitioners, grant diplomas to dispensers, and take part in postgraduate medical education (Chapter 11).

Some Eminent Apothecaries

Gideon Delaune

Gideon de Laune (Delaune) (Fig. 13) was born in 1565 in Rheims, the son of a Protestant pastor, William de Laune, who had studied medicine in Paris and Montpellier. Some time between 1575 and 1580 the family moved to London, where William practised medicine and, in 1582, became a Licentiate of the College of Physicians.[21] Gideon trained as an apothecary and prospered, especially by importing rare drugs and spices and by marrying a wealthy Frenchwoman, Judith Chamberlaine, a member of the famous family of 'man-midwives' (p. 123). They had a son and a daughter, both of whom 'married well'. Gideon's younger brother, Paul, became a Fellow of the College of Physicians.

If not the actual founder of the Society of Apothecaries, Gideon Delaune was very influential in its creation. He was apothecary to King James I and his Queen, Anne of Denmark and was in close touch with one of the King's physicians, Sir Theodore de Mayerne (p. 19). Delaune was one of the Assistants named in the Charter. He became Under Warden of the Society in 1624 and Upper Warden shortly thereafter but, as a foreigner, could not become Master without a special provision, made at the King's request, that he be made a Freeman of the City of London.[22] He was elected Master in 1628 and again, after taking English nationality, in 1637. He died in 1659.

Delaune worked hard for the Society. In 1618 he was one of the Assistants delegated to prepare a schedule of the medicines required by an apothecary and in 1620 he successfully opposed a Bill to establish a Company of Distillers, which the apothecaries thought would be detrimental to their interests.[23] He was a generous benefactor to the Society and his professional reputation was such that 'Delaune's pill', a secret preparation of which the active principle was probably colocynth, was in great demand even in the eighteenth century.

John Parkinson

John Parkinson was another apothecary, whose name appeared in the first list of Assistants in the Charter of the Society of Apothecaries. He was elected a Warden in 1620 but resigned shortly thereafter. He was apothecary to King James I and 'King's botanist' to Charles I. Parkinson was not only a leading apothecary but also a practical gardener and an active writer on herbs and their medicinal use.[24] In this book, *The Theater of Plants* (1640), he described about 3800 plants.

Figure 13. Gideon Delaune (courtesy of the Worshipful Society of Apothecaries of London.)

Thomas Johnson

Another London apothecary, Thomas Johnson, was a pupil of Parkinson and kept a small garden, in which he grew rare plants. He took an active part in the Society's botanical excursions for training apprentices and, in 1633, brought out an enlarged edition of Gerard's *Herball*. When he presented a copy of this monumental tome to the Society he was made a Liveryman and presented with the appropriate gown and hood.[25] He published his own herbal, *Mercurius botanicus*, in 1634.

At the outbreak of the First Civil War Johnson joined the Royalist army where he rose to the rank of lieutenant-colonel and died of wounds sustained in the defence of Basing House in Hampshire.

Nicolas Lefevre

Nicolas le Fèvre (Lefevre) qualified as an apothecary at the University of Sedan and practised in Paris and then in London, where he became Apothecary in Ordinary to King Charles II. His *Traité de la chymie* (1661), the 5th edition of which was published under the title *Cours de chymie*, was considered the best textbook of chemistry of the period and was translated into several languages, including English.[26] Lefevre himself translated Sir Thomas Browne's *Religio medici* into French. He was a founder member of the Royal Society.[27]

Nicholas Culpeper

One of the most controversial figures of the seventeenth-century medical world, Nicholas Culpeper, practised as an apothecary though not a member of the Society. Although apprenticed in 1634 to Stephen Higgins, a previous Master of the Society, he never completed his training. He served in the Parliamentary army in the First Civil War and then practised as an 'astrologer and physician' in Spitalfields.[28] His professional life was a running battle with the College of Physicians, which attacked him as a quack and was counter-attacked in vigorous prose as a group of incompetent practitioners. Although not a qualified apothecary he had a profound influence on the use of drugs.

Culpeper described many medicinal herbs in his first book, *A Physicall Directory* (1649), later expanded into *The English Physitian Enlarged* (1653), which included an English translation of the *Pharmacopoea Londinensis* (p. 5), with comments, often derogatory, on its contents and its compilers. He was a firm believer in astrology and believed, at a time when astrology was becoming less popular with physicians, that each medicinal herb is associated with a particular planet, which determines its therapeutic use. In a later edition of the Pharmacopoeia, *The London Dispensatory* (1683), Culpeper describes the preparation and use of many medicines, often distinguishing between the recommendation of the College of Physicians and his own. One which he favours is 'the Skull of a man that was never buried, being beaten to Powder, and given inwardly, the quantity of a dram at a time in Betany water'; this 'helps Palsies and Falling-sickness'.[29] As author he describes himself as 'Nich. Culpeper Gent. Student in Physick and Astrology'. Culpeper's work was so popular that it was reprinted even into the nineteenth century.

William Salmon

A younger contemporary of Culpeper, William Salmon, was another popular, though unqualified writer on pharmacy; he describes himself as 'Professor of Physic', though he had no medical qualification. Salmon brought out a *New London Dispensatory* in 1678, which ran to several editions, and, in a later book, *Seplasium: the Compleat Physician or the Druggists Shop Open'd*, he listed the essential qualities of a good medicine: it must be 'cheap, common, easily prepared, effectual, safe, durable, small in dose'[30], all useful attributes.

Status of the Apothecary

When the Society of Apothecaries split off from the Grocers' Company some of the grocers continued to manufacture and trade in drugs, though they remained in the Grocers' Company, and some apothecaries limited their activities to preparing and selling drugs. Other apothecaries, who were more concerned with treating patients, came to rely on these 'drug-sters' (druggists) for their supplies. The main difference between apothecary and druggist was that the latter did not leave his shop. By the end of the seventeenth century many remedies were manufactured by chemists and the 'chemist and druggist' became an important tradesman, although without professional standing until the Pharmaceutical Society was founded in 1841, uniting the pharmaceutical apothecaries with the chemists and druggists.

After the Civil Wars, according to a historian of the period: 'The apothecaries seem to have been mainly sons of small shopkeepers, yeomen, and respectable craftsmen. In towns the practising apothecary was of low status but in the country, where he was usually the only doctor, he was sometimes a man of good family.'[31] Retail trade was not despised in the seventeenth or eighteenth centuries; social snobbery against it dates from the nineteenth century and reached a peak in Victorian times.

The creation of the Society of Apothecaries in 1617 gave the London apothecaries professional status, which extended to other centres, though only in London were there enough apothecaries to form a Society. The founders of the Society of Apothecaries were intelligent and prudent men, who co-operated with the powerful College of Physicians and established the Society in the public eye as a respectable organisation. Apothecaries took part in the founding of the Royal Society (p. 70) and contributed to its Transactions, especially in the fields of botany and chemistry. Among those elected to the Royal Society in the seventeenth century were Nicholas Lefevre (p. 98), John Haughton, Samuel Doody, and James Petiver.[32]

Relations with the physicians were sometimes strained because the physicians objected to the apothecaries dispensing medicine without a physician's prescription and the apothecaries objected to the physicians dispensing their own medicines. The Great Plague (p. 154) increased the popularity of the apothecaries because most of them stayed in London and treated plague victims, whereas most of the physicians followed their wealthy patients out of the city.[33] T. F. Barnard, apothecary to St Bartholomew's Hospital, remained at his post and treated the patients when the physicians left;[34] he was already the resident doctor in the hospital, equivalent to the modern 'houseman', responsible for the care of patients between the physicians' visits. William Boghurst, another apothecary who visited and treated plague patients, wrote from his personal experience one of the best accounts of the Great Plague.[35] He was 34 years old at the time and lived to the age of 54.

As the century advanced the number of qualified physicians became more and more inadequate for the medical needs of the expanding population. By 1701 there were more than five times as many apothecaries as physicians in London. By this time the general practitioner was either an apothecary or a barber-surgeon or, less commonly, an individual with both qualifications. Legally the apothecary was allowed to charge only for the medicines supplied and not for his advice; in practice the cost of the medicine included any other services rendered.

CHAPTER 7

Surgery

A LTHOUGH IN THE SEVENTEENTH CENTURY there was a marked social
and professional distinction between physicians and surgeons, this had
not always been the case. From ancient times to the early Middle Ages
the same individual would normally practise both medicine and surgery.
At the end of the Middle Ages and during the Renaissance and Reformation
some specialisation occurred, especially in towns, and by the seventeenth
century the English physician would not normally perform surgery. Most
medical practitioners then were surgeons, who also practised medicine
though often not legally entitled to do so, or apothecaries, who might
perform simple operations such as venesection

The Legacy of Earlier Surgery

Ancient surgery

Surgery is probably as old as medicine. Many neolithic skulls have trephine
holes with evidence of subsequent bone growth, which proves that the
patient survived the operation.[1] Although we cannot tell now why trephi-
nation was performed we know that it was not usually to relieve pressure
on the brain due to injury, as there is seldom any sign of fracture of the
skull. The operation is still performed today, usually for the relief of high
intracranial pressure. An ancient Egyptian hieroglyph (*c.* 2400 BC) depicts
the operation of circumcision.[2]

In Babylon the Code of Hammurabi (*c.* 1740 BC) described some surgical
operations, laid down the fees to be charged, which varied with the wealth
and social status of the patient, and decreed the sometimes severe penalties
for failure.[3] Understandably, the surgeons of the time were unwilling to
undertake any operation hazardous to both patient and surgeon. The Edwin
Smith papyrus (*c.* 1600 BC), which deals mainly with surgery, contains
forty-eight case histories of wounds, fractures, dislocations, and tu-

mours,[4] with a detailed description of the treatment, where treatment was practicable, and advice against intervention when the outlook was poor.

Greek surgery

Early Greek writings refer to army surgeons, skilled in dressing and bandaging wounds, and the Hippocratic school (p. 37) was expert at wound surgery, using clean, or even boiled, water and dressings of new linen.[5] The operator had to have clean hands and nails, and fresh wounds were expected to heal 'by first intention' (without suppurating). The Hippocratic corpus describes wound surgery, trephining, and the reduction of fractures and dislocations of limbs and of the jaw. Operations were performed also on eyes, ears, nose and teeth, and piles were treated with the cautery or excised.

Roman surgery

The *De medicina* of Celsus (p. 39) is the first Latin treatise on surgery as well as on medicine.[6] Celsus describes the arrest of bleeding by pressure and the ligature of veins and arteries in the groin during the operation of castration. He describes the operation for hernia, returning the extruded bowel to the abdominal cavity and tying and excising the sac, essentially the modern operation without the additional procedures adopted today to prevent recurrence. Piles, fistula, fractures and dislocations were treated effectively and tumours excised. The technique of tonsillectomy is described, as is 'couching for the cataract', which involves pressing the opaque lens down with a needle into the lower part of the eye. Plastic surgery was also used, as it had been in ancient India, to reconstruct the nose or ear with flaps of skin from another part of the body.[7]

Celsus's method of 'cutting for the stone' (lithotomy) was employed for so many centuries that it is worth describing. With the patient held in a 'jack-knife' position the surgeon put his left forefinger into the anus and his right hand on the lower abdomen, forcing the stone down into the grip of the left forefinger; an incision was then made down to the stone, which was then pushed out by the left forefinger or, if it was very large, extracted with a hook. The wound was not sutured but dressed with wool and warm oil and usually healed satisfactorily.[8]

Celsus recommended administration of mandrake (*Atropa mandragora*) and henbane (*Hyoscyamus niger*) before the operation to relieve pain, and poppy (*Papaver somniferum*), which contains opium, had been used from earlier times for this purpose.[9]

Roman army surgeons performed amputations with flaps of healthy tissue to cover the stump instead of the previous, less satisfactory, circular method, which was still employed when gangrene was present.[10] Bleeding was controlled with ligatures or by cautery. Wounded soldiers were treated, as far as possible, in the field by their companions, some of whom (*medici*) had gained experience in treating wounds. The more seriously injured were treated in hospitals (*valetudinaria*), which were well planned, with adequate sanitation, and served both sick and wounded; these were the precursors of the monastic hospitals of the Middle Ages.[11]

Although primarily a physician, Galen (p. 39) had been surgeon to a school of gladiators, so had considerable experience of wound surgery. He described some new operations, such as resection of part of a rib to facilitate drainage of pus from inside the chest,[12] a procedure still practised in the twentieth century. Galen expected wounds to suppurate and regarded this as essential to healing, a mistaken view still widely held in the seventeenth century.

The Middle Ages

The first independent work on surgery of the Middle Ages, written in Arabic by Albucasis in the tenth century, has illustrations of more than 200 surgical instruments and descriptions of new as well as of traditional operations. Albucasis used cautery for a wide variety of ailments ranging from cataract to cancer; it had long been used to arrest bleeding from wounds.[13] The book was translated into Latin (*De chirurgia*) and widely read.

Although priests were forbidden by the Council of Tours (1163) to shed blood and so could not legitimately practise surgery, and this prohibition was repeated by the fourth Lateran Council (1215), many continued to practise without interference. In the thirteenth century Theodoric, Bishop of Cervia, wrote a *Chyrurgia*, in which he recommended the use of simple dressings for wounds, which he believed should be kept clean and should not suppurate.[14] In spite of the success of this technique most surgeons continued to apply dirty and irritant materials or scalding oil to wounds until simple clean treatment was revived by Ambroise Paré in the sixteenth century.

The greatest surgeons of the fourteenth century were two Frenchmen, Henri de Mondeville and Guy de Chauliac. De Mondeville was surgeon to two kings of France (Philip IV and Louis X) and lectured in anatomy at the University of Montpellier. He was one of the few surgeons of the time to follow the advice of Theodoric that wounds should be kept clean and should not suppurate; if a wound was clean he closed it with sutures. Unfortunately his *Cyrurgia*, the first French textbook of surgery,[15] though widely circulated in manuscript, was not translated into French and printed until 1892.

The most famous surgeon of the Middle Ages, Guy de Chauliac, studied at Montpellier and Bologna and was medical adviser and chaplain to Pope Clement VI and two of his successors. His methods are described in his book, *Cyrurgia magna* (1363), which was translated into French, Italian, Dutch, German, Spanish and English and was regarded as an authoritative text until the eighteenth century.[16] De Chauliac quotes Hippocrates, Galen, Rhazes, Avicenna and Albucasis but adds ideas of his own, including an operation for radical cure of hernia and the use of extension to prevent shortening of a fractured limb.[17] Unfortunately, his treatment of wounds reverted to the galenic application of ointments and plasters, which delay rather than assist healing, and his influence was such that this was the commonest method of treatment for the next two centuries.

Two types of septic wound might be inflicted intentionally by the surgeon to 'evacuate superfluous humours' and were still in use in the seventeenth century. An 'issue' was a small ulcer made by a hot iron, lancet, or caustic and a 'seton' was a strip of silk or linen drawn through a fold of skin and left in position except for daily movement from side to side to promote drainage of pus.[18]

The only English surgeon of note during this period, John of Arderne, studied at Montpellier, where he learnt the methods of Henri de Mondeville, and practised in France and later in England. He is best known for his treatment of anal fistula, previously believed incurable, by opening it widely and checking bleeding by pressure, essentially the method employed today.[19] Arderne was widely employed by the aristocracy as a general surgeon. Like other students of Henri de Mondeville he applied simple, clean dressings to wounds and changed them infrequently.

The medieval surgeon would not normally operate on wounds of the brain, heart, lungs, bladder, stomach or small intestine, which Hippocrates had said were invariably fatal, without an undertaking that he would not be held responsible for the patient's death.

Renaissance and Reformation

Wound surgery was complicated from mid-fourteenth century by the increasing use of firearms, which caused more damage and infection than simpler weapons. Wounds were sometimes enlarged by the surgeon to remove damaged tissue, bleeding was checked by hot irons or scalding oil, and dirty applications ensured that the wound would suppurate. The greatest advance in wound surgery, before Joseph Lister's antiseptic technique in the nineteenth century, was due to a French military surgeon, Ambroise Paré, who found that wounds healed better and the patient was spared much pain if a mixture of egg yolk, oil of roses, and turpentine was applied instead of the customary scalding oil, and bleeding was arrested by tying blood vessels instead of by cautery.[20]

Paré qualified as a barber-surgeon in Paris in 1541. He had considerable experience on battlefields and published his conservative method of wound treatment in 1545 as *La méthode de traicter les playes faictes par hacquebutes* (arquebuses). Although of humble origin and a Huguenot he became surgeon-in-ordinary to four kings of France and was spared at the Massacre of St Bartholomew by direct order of King Charles IX.[21] Paré wrote many books, all in French so that they were comprehensible to French surgeons, many of whom could not read Latin; the books were translated into many languages and were influential in the seventeenth century. Paré was a deeply religious man and his best-known comment after successful treatment of a wounded soldier was: '*Je le pansay, Dieu le guarit.*'[22]

The first major advance in the operation of 'cutting for the stone' (lithotomy) since the time of Celsus (p. 39) was the 'Marian technique', described in 1535 by Mariano Santo of Naples. He inserted a grooved staff through the urethra into the bladder, cut down on it, and introduced forceps through the wound into the bladder to grasp and extract the stone or stones.[23] In 1556 a French surgeon, Pierre Franco, was the first to remove a bladder stone through the abdominal wall (suprapubic lithotomy) but he did not recommend the technique for general use.[24] Lithotomy was more often performed by itinerant quacks, specialising in this operation, than by general surgeons.

Also in the sixteenth century Gaspare Tagliacozzi of Bologna, commonly regarded as the founder of modern plastic surgery, reconstructed noses and ears with flaps of the patient's own skin.[25] These operations were in considerable demand in the seventeenth century since the judicial penalty for some crimes was cutting off the nose or ear, and loss of the bridge of the nose was a common complication of syphilis. They had been performed in ancient India and were mentioned by Celsus but had fallen into disuse until revived by the Brancas in Sicily in the fifteenth century. For rhinoplasty (repair of the nose) Antonio Branca and Tagliacozzi took the flap from an arm, which was kept in contact with the nose until the flap had established a blood supply from that organ, when its connection with the arm could be severed and the new nose moulded appropriately.

An English surgeon, Thomas Vicary, surgeon to King Henry VIII, Edward VI, Queen Mary and Elizabeth I and to St Bartholomew's Hospital in London was the author of the first textbook of anatomy to be written in English, which was part of his book, *The Englishmans Treasure, or Treasor for Englishmen: With the true Anatomye of Mans Body* (1548). Although the anatomy was uninspired and unoriginal the professional and social standards Vicary set for the surgeon were high; he must be good-looking, well mannered, learned, expert, ingenious, moral, honest and discreet.[26] He should reject incurable cases and be good to the poor. Although admired at the time as a successful surgeon, Vicary's claim to fame is the part he played in establishing the Company of Barber-Surgeons (p. 108).

Two other sixteenth-century English surgeons, Thomas Gale and William Clowes, had considerable military experience and wrote on gunshot wounds but their treatment was inferior to Paré's. Perhaps the most influential book on the subject at the beginning of the seventeenth century was by the Scotsman, Peter Lowe, *The Whole Course of Chirurgerie*, first published in 1597.

The Organisation of Surgery

Early guilds

English barber-surgeons and surgeons had been organised in guilds as early as the fourteenth century, the object of a guild being to protect the interests of its members and of the public. In London the guilds concerned with the practice of surgery were the Company of Barbers, later called the Barber-Surgeons' Company, and the Fellowship of Surgeons, a smaller and more elite body whose members practised only surgery.[27] Disputes between these two bodies and with the College of Physicians were common. The barber-surgeons owned premises in London, Barbers' Hall, as early as the fifteenth century and anatomical dissections were performed there in the sixteenth century.

The Barber-Surgeons' Company

The king's surgeon, Thomas Vicary (p. 107) was largely responsible for persuading Henry VIII to grant a charter in 1540, uniting the Barber-Surgeons' Company and the Fellowship of Surgeons in one company, the 'Mystery and Comminalte of Barbours and Surgeons of London', with Vicary as the first Master. In the new Company the barbers were no longer allowed to practise surgery, except drawing teeth, and the surgeons were no longer barbers.[28] The Company comprised a Master and three Wardens, the Master being barber or surgeon in alternate years, the Livery (full members) and the Court of Assistants.[29]

The Company was responsible for training and licensing surgeons and had authority to fine unlicensed practitioners in London. It was entitled to receive four bodies of executed criminals each year for dissection and surgeon members of the Company were required to attend anatomical lectures and dissections. Admission to membership was by examination after the usual seven-year period of apprenticeship but, as in medicine, a licence to practise surgery could be granted by the Bishop of London or the Dean of St Paul's (p. 6). Women could be licensed but were not eligible for the Livery.[30]

Surgeons' guilds of the seventeenth century

The Company of Barber-Surgeons was the official organisation of surgeons in London during the seventeenth century. In 1637 the Company's Hall now 'Surgeons' Hall', was rebuilt with the addition of an anatomical theatre for dissections, the only part of the building to survive the Great Fire of 1666.[31] In 1684 the surgeons petitioned King Charles II for formal separation from the barbers but this was not granted until 1745, when barbers and surgeons were again separated into two independent companies.

Some surgeons' guilds in other towns differed in a number of respects from the London Company (p. 7), but the purpose of them all was to restrict the practice of surgery to trained and qualified practitioners and to raise the status of the surgeon. In a Royal Charter of 1629 it was decreed that all British ships must carry a surgeon approved by the London Company and the Company was responsible for his equipment[32] (medical as well as surgical because the ships did not carry a physician).

Brief Lives of Some Surgeons

John Woodall

The leading English surgeon under the early Stuarts was John Woodall, born in Warwick about 1570, who began his surgical career in the wars with France, served in ships, and was admitted to the Barber-Surgeons' Company in 1601. He married in 1603, had at least ten children, and outlived his wife.

As the first surgeon-general of the East India Company, when it was organised on a joint-stock basis in 1612, Woodall drew up regulations for the Company's surgeons and lists of instruments and medicines for their chests. The first edition of his book, *The Surgions Mate* (1617) was written in collaboration with a physician and an apothecary and was the standard book of reference for ships' surgeons throughout the century.[33] Woodall listed the 'particular ingredients' for a surgeon's chest and their uses and described the care of wounds, the treatment of abscesses, ulcers and fistulas, the cure of fractures and dislocations, and the technique of amputation, in which he sacrificed as little of the limb as possible and preferred ligatures to cautery to stop bleeding. He also invented the modern trephine with crown and central pin. Some of the instruments he used are depicted in Fig. 14.

Woodall also recommended the juice of lemons, failing which limes or oranges, for the prevention and treatment of scurvy,[34] a disease which was responsible for much sickness and death on long voyages and is now known to be due to lack of vitamin C, which is contained in fresh fruit and vegetables. Woodall's recommendation was not generally adopted, although its efficacy was confirmed by James Lind in *A Treatise of the Scurvy* (1753), until Gilbert Blane introduced it into the Royal Navy in 1796 and, by so doing, abolished scurvy in that service. Woodall also prepared and described a preparation, *Aurum vitae*, which he claimed to be an effective antidote against plague.[35] He set up a dockside hospital for the East India Company at Blackwall (now Poplar) and was a surgeon on the staff of St

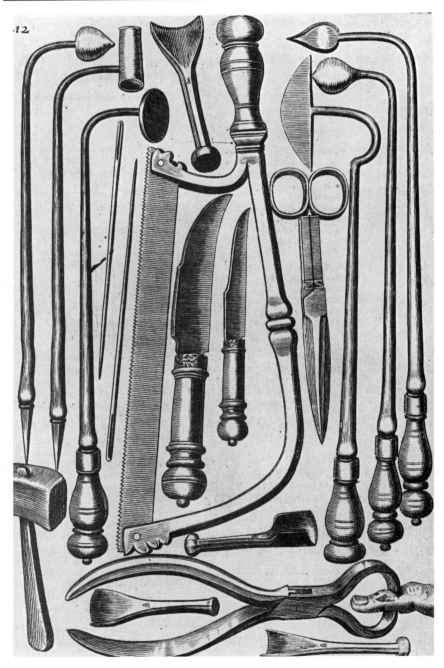

Figure 14. Some of John Woodall's surgical instruments (courtesy of the Royal College of Surgeons of England)

Bartholomew's Hospital while William Harvey was physician (p. 13). Woodall protested repeatedly against the monopoly of medical practice in London by the College of Physicians.

Woodall participated actively in commercial ventures, not only with the East India Company but also with the Drapers' Company, Virginia Company and others. He acquired property in Virginia and Bermuda and was involved in much litigation, most of it successful. In 1633 he was elected Master of the Barber-Surgeons' Company, in spite of censure for abusive language and absence from meetings.[36] He died in 1643.

Richard Wiseman

Richard Wiseman, the outstanding surgeon of the century (Fig. 15), was born about 1622 but no record of the place or date of his birth or of his parentage is known, which suggests that he may have been an illegitimate child.[37] He was apprenticed in 1637 to a barber-surgeon in London and entered the Dutch Navy as a surgeon in 1643. In 1644 he joined the Royalist army in the First Civil War and served under the Prince of Wales, eventually accompanying him to France. He returned to Scotland with the Prince after the execution of Charles I in 1649, joined in his unsuccessful invasion of England, was captured at the battle of Worcester, and spent two years as a prisoner of war. On his release he was admitted to the Company of Barber-Surgeons but, as a known royalist, he was under suspicion by the authorities, imprisoned again, and in some danger of his life. When he was released he took service with the Spanish Navy until the Restoration, when he returned to London as Surgeon-in-Ordinary to King Charles II. By this time his health was poor and, although he lived for another sixteen years, he spent more of his time writing than practising surgery. Wiseman married twice, though the details are not known, and his second wife bore him a posthumous son, his only child.[38] He died in 1676.

From his wide experience of war surgery Wiseman stressed the importance of removing foreign bodies (including clothing) from wounds and bringing the edges together. He covered gunshot wounds with oil-soaked linen and he was reluctant to amputate limbs although, when it was necessary, he would do so without delay.

In heat of Fight, whether it be at Sea or Land, the Chirurgeon ought to consider at the first Dressing, what possibility there is of preserving

Figure 15. Richard Wiseman (courtesy of the Royal College of Surgeons of England)

the wounded Member; and accordingly, if there be no hope of saving it, to make his amputation at that instant whilst the Patient is free of Fever &c.[39]

Wiseman found that most penetrating wounds of the chest or abdomen were fatal.

A Treatise of Wounds (1672) and *Severall Chirurgicall Treatises* (1676), eight in number published in the year of his death, are a record of his own surgical experience.

> I do pretend to have spent my time in Armies, Navies and Cities, not in Universities; Nor to have been much conversant in Books, through my constant Employment in, and the little leisure I had from my Profession, till my want of health in late years enforced me to make them my diversion.[40]

*The Chirurgicall Treatise*s deal with tumours, ulcers, diseases of the anus, the king's evil, wounds, gunshot wounds, fractures and dislocations, and venereal disease; much of the treatment Wiseman recommends would be acceptable today. He believed in the royal touch for the king's evil (p. 66) but was prepared to excise the affected glands in the neck: 'It is not necessary that a Disease, which is cured by Miracle, should be remediable by no rules of Art.'[41] Wiseman describes syphilis, 'a venemous contagious Disease gotten either Immediately or Mediately from an impure Coition';[42] a child can get it from parent or nurse. He affirms that it is not due to disordered humours but to a venom, producing first local and then general effects; the most effective treatment is with mercury.

Joseph Binns

Joseph Binns, another London surgeon, moved in less exalted circles than Woodall or Wiseman since most of his patients belonged to the middle class or lower, but fortunately he kept a case-book from 1633 to 1663, in which he recorded particulars of 671 cases. It has never been printed but the manuscript is preserved in the British Library and has recently been studied in detail by Lucinda Beier. Our knowledge of Binns starts in 1637, when he joined the Company of Barber-Surgeons.[43] In 1647 he joined the staff of St Bartholomew's Hospital and he worked there and in private practice until his death in 1664. He was married and had at least three children and was well off financially. In 1662 and 1663 he was a Warden of the Barber-Surgeons' Company.

Binns's practice included treatment of abscesses, fistulas, fractures, hernias, piles, tumours, and venereal disease. Sometimes the patient's progress was recorded; it might be 'well, laus deo' or 'dyed'.[44] Like Wiseman, Binns believed in the royal touch for the King's evil but, also like Wiseman, he operated on the diseased glands.[45]

A large proportion of Binns's practice was casualty surgery on patients suffering domestic or occupational (including battle) injuries. A dramatic example of an occupational injury was to a builder who fell three storeys and suffered only a broken collar-bone and a bruise on the back of his head, with delirium for a day and a night.[46] In general Binns stitched clean wounds but kept dirty ones open for pus to escape. He usually prescribed a laxative or an enema and a light diet but seldom let blood. He very rarely amputated a limb, even when it was heavily infected; indeed one patient who died of gangrene might have been saved by an amputation.[47]

Binns did not 'cut for the stone' or act as a 'man–midwife', but he treated cases of headache, diarrhoea, colic and other medical conditions with internal remedies, which were supposed to be prescribed only by a physician. He treated many cases of syphilis, with varying success. 'An apparent Cure for the French Disease' contained sarsaparilla and guaiacum (both imported from South America) and mithridate (p. 40) in wine and beer,[48] but he treated most of these patients with mercury and, when necessary, tried to relieve the symptoms of mercury poisoning.[49] Although most of his practice was surgical Joseph Binns, like most surgeons of his time, was really a general practitioner.

The Scope of Surgery

Venesection

Probably the commonest task performed by the surgeon in the seventeenth century, although it might also be performed by an apothecary or by a physician, was venesection (p. 59). Blood-letting was regarded as the primary treatment for many injuries as well as diseases and would often be performed by the surgeon on his own initiative although, except in the treatment of wounds, he was required by law to act under the direction of a physician. Venesection probably contributed to the death of many patients, especially if they had already lost blood through injury.

Wound surgery

Wound surgery made little progress in the seventeenth century; it was still based largely on tradition and even superstition. In 'sympathetic treatment' of a wound the healing ointment was applied not to the wound but to the weapon (p. 142). Suppuration was to be expected since all open wounds were infected; in the case of gunshot wounds, as Wiseman had observed (p. 111), this would persist until the missile and any clothing carried with it into the wound had been removed. Wiseman stitched large wounds but, as might be done today, left a lower orifice for draining the wound.[50] He used sutures, cautery, or caustic drugs to arrest bleeding. He noted that in head wounds the brain should, if possible, be kept within its membranes but any depression of the skull must be elevated to relieve pressure on the brain.[51] Abdominal wounds were treated by repairing and replacing the gut and closing the abdominal wall with deep stitches to prevent subsequent hernia.[52] Penetrating chest wounds were usually fatal and there was no effective treatment. All wounds were dressed with a boiled non-oily lotion.

Wounds might be left open to heal from below but the Scottish surgeon, Alexander Read, who was also a Fellow of the College of Physicians (a most unusual combination of qualifications) and a lecturer at the Barber-Surgeons' Hall, brought together the edges of large wounds with sutures and closed small wounds by stitching together strips of cloth glued to the edges.[53] When bleeding was not severe Read arrested it by applying pledgets of lint or tow moistened with beaten white of eggs or with a mixture of vinegar and water, but if bleeding was from a large artery or vein he tied the vessel with strong silk thread.[54] Another barber-surgeon, Thomas Bonham, prescribed a lotion for a 'wound made with sharpe pointed weapons'; it contained terebinth, gum acacia, euphorbia, aloes, cinnamon and some other herbs, powdered and made into an infusion.[55]

The treatment of almost any serious limb wound was amputation. Woodall favoured the traditional circular method but James Yonge, in *A New Way of Amputation* (1679), part of a larger work, *Currus triumphalis è terebinthô*, in which he recommends the application of oil of terebinth to wounds, revived the more satisfactory flap method, which had been neglected for centuries, and improved it by using a single flap.

> The Ligatures and Gripe [tourniquets and grip upon the limb by assistants] being made after the common manner you are with your Catlin or some long incision-knife, to raise (suppose it the Leg) a flap

of the membranous flesh covering the muscles of the Calf, beginning below the place where you intend to make excision and raising it thitherward of length enought [sic] to cover the stump. Having done so turn it back under the hand of him that gripes and, as soon as you have severed the member, bring the flap of cutaneous flesh over the stump and fasten it to the edges thereof by four or five strong stitches and, having so done, slap a dossil [plug] of lint into the inferior part, that one passage may be open for any blood or matter that may lodge between.[56]

Lithotomy

Bladder stone was still a prevalent and painful complaint in the seventeenth century and 'cutting for the stone' was still commonly performed, as it had been in the Middle Ages, by specialists in the operation. The general surgeon, Joseph Binns, did not cut for the stone (p. 114) but some others did so. The commonest technique was the Marian operation (p. 106) and there was no major advance until William Cheselden, in the next century, introduced a faster and safer technique.[57]

Other surgical operations

Apart from casualty surgery and operations which had been performed since ancient times, such as cutting for the stone and couching for cataract (p. 103), operations performed successfully in England in the seventeenth century included the treatment of hare-lip and of wryneck, both usually by quacks.[58] Wiseman operated successfully on aneurysm (localised dilatation of an artery) by tying the artery above the aneurysm and removing the clotted blood inside.[59] He treated extensive burns by covering them with lint dipped in oil of bitter almonds, oil of elders, egg-yolk, stramonium, and other substances.[60]

The physician, Thomas Willis (p. 17), treated a case of achalasia (failure of the lower end of the gullet to relax) by giving his patient a whalebone rod with a round button at the end for pushing food into his stomach; this worked well for fifteen years.[61]

An excellent description of the state of the art of surgery, as well as of medicine, in the seventeenth century was *The Institutions of the Whole Art both of Physick and Chirurgery* (1646) by Daniel Sennert of Wittenberg, translated into English from the original Latin in 1658 and widely read. He described the instruments required by a surgeon and observed that fractures must be realigned before splinting and that splints might be of wood, pasteboard or leather.[62] The lips of a narrow wound could be brought together by bandaging but a larger one required sutures. Abscesses should be opened and corrupted parts cut away. Sennert describes the reconstruction of nose, lip and ear, very much as they were performed in the previous century by Tagliacozzi (p. 106).

Anaesthesia

The relief of pain during operations, which had been attempted in ancient times (p. 103), was not taken very seriously in the seventeenth century. A 'soporific sponge', soaked in herbs (including the traditional mandrake, opium and henbane), might be applied to the nostrils (where it would have very little effect), but more usually the patient was given alcohol to drink before the operation.[63] This could reduce anxiety but has very little pain-killing action. Lacking anaesthesia the speed of operation was an important factor so that the period of acute suffering could be kept as short as possible. The best surgeons worked fast.

The success of surgery

Although Wiseman described his unsuccessful as well as his successful cases the results of most surgical operations were not recorded and can only be surmised. Penetrating wounds of head, chest or abdomen were usually fatal, as were limb wounds with extensive bone damage, unless prompt amputation was performed. Lithotomy (cutting for the stone) was often successful and uncomplicated, superficial tumours might be removed and plastic surgery (especially for the reconstruction of the nose) was often effective. Operations were usually performed in the patient's house or in that of a friend. Samuel Pepys was 'cut of the stone' in a friend's house in 1658.[64]

Surgical treatment in hospital was very dangerous because of the high incidence of infected wounds and the lack of effective measures to prevent the spread of infection. Since there were few hospitals in the seventeenth century this was not the major social problem which it became in the eighteenth and nineteenth centuries.

Status of the Surgeon

Although the surgeon ranked below the physician both socially and professionally and lacked the physician's obligatory study of the classics, he
was by no means uneducated and his professional training as an apprentice
and as a student at the Barber-Surgeons' Hall was superior to that of the
contemporary physician. Membership of a guild, the Barber-Surgeons'
Company, gave him civic status and, in the seventeenth century, the
Company was providing surgeons for the East India Company and for the
Royal Navy. Although on land the surgeon was supposed to treat internal
ailments only under direction by a physician, this was obviously impracticable at sea and in country districts, where no physician was available.
Even in London most of what we would now call general practice was
performed by apothecaries or surgeons and there were more surgeons than
apothecaries.[65]

A leading surgeon might perform fewer operations than others because,
if employed by a wealthy patient, the contract might require him to live
in the patient's house until his recovery. His fee might depend on the
success of the operation but his life would not be forfeit if he failed. The
heads of the profession, such as John Woodall and Richard Wiseman, were
educated, intelligent, and fit company for royalty. The status of others
depended largely on the success of their practice but was usually higher
in rural areas, where the surgeon was the only doctor, than in cities.

CHAPTER 8

Midwives And Nurses

IN THE SEVENTEENTH CENTURY midwifery was usually performed by women, who might or might not have some training in the art and might or might not have a certificate of competence from the local bishop. Their technique was crude and unhygienic and maternal mortality was high. Some medical practitioners conducted a few confinements but the man-midwife was uncommon and the medically qualified specialist obstetrician even rarer. Not until the nineteenth century were obstetrics and gynaecology included in conventional medical training.

Early Midwifery

'That the practice of midwifery . . . is the most ancient branch of medicine is shown by the fact that, as a result of long continuance of artificial assistance, the instinctive conduct of her own labour is no longer part of a woman's natural endowment.'[1] Whether midwifery can claim priority over medicine and surgery is questionable but the argument supports its claim to be a very ancient practice.

Greek obstetrics and gynaecology

The Hippocratic corpus describes displacements of the womb, including prolapse, which might be corrected manually, and disorders of menstruation, for which particular herbs were recommended to promote or reduce the menstrual flow.[2] Herbs used to promote menstruation included fennel, myrrh, sage and rue; to reduce it bark of oak or of acacia was applied locally. Other herbs, such as wormwood or dittany, were administered to promote expulsion of the placenta after the birth of the child and were still prescribed for this purpose in the seventeenth century.[3] A dead fetus might be destroyed and extracted piecemeal to save the mother's life or a Caesarian section performed to extract a living child from a dead mother.

The leading writer of ancient times on obstetrics, gynaecology and paediatrics was a physician, Soranus of Ephesus (second century AD).[4] Soranus described the correction of some malpresentations of the fetus and recommended early manual removal of the placenta after labour, which was still the usual practice in the seventeenth century.

The Middle Ages

After Soranus there was no important advance in midwifery for fourteen centuries. An eleventh-century Latin manuscript attributed to a woman doctor, Trotula, of the school of Salerno was the standard medieval text but added little to previous knowledge.

The sixteenth century

The first formal control of midwives in England was an Act of 1512, requiring them to be licensed by the local bishop on the recommendation of responsible neighbours. Women practising without a licence could be fined or excommunicated. The licensed midwife took an oath not to practise witchcraft, demand an abnormal fee, or arrange for secret burial of a stillborn infant; she must baptise a dying infant if no priest was available.[5]

The first book on midwifery published in England was *The Byrth of Mankynde* (1540), a translation by Richard Jones of a Latin translation of a German book, *Der swangern Frawen und hebammen Rosegarten* (1513) by Eucharius Rösslin the elder, state physician of Worms and Frankfurt-am-Main.[6] The book described different presentations of the fetus and how to conduct the delivery in each case. Although it added little to medieval practice it ran to many editions and was translated into French, and Italian as well as Latin and English. The best-known English version in the seventeenth century was Thomas Raynalde's translation, first published in 1545.

The works of Ambroise Paré (p. 106), including a section on midwifery published in Paris in 1549, were first translated into English in 1634.[7] Improved procedures were described for the conduct of normal and of abnormal labour.

Seventeenth Century Midwifery

Midwives and man-midwives

Many seventeenth-century midwives were illiterate and very few kept records of their cases. Some physicians or surgeons who practised midwifery wrote books on the subject, usually with detailed instructions for the conduct of normal and of abnormal labour.

James Rueff, the first English man-midwife of note in the seventeenth century, described himself as 'a learned and expert Chirurgion'. In his book, *The Expert Midwife* (1631), 'written in English for the benefit of midwives, most of whom are unlearned', he describes the development of the embryo and notes that, according to the Church, it receives its soul on the forty-first day and becomes an infant.[8] The mother must be protected from fright, over-activity and witchcraft[9]. Rueff shared the popular belief that hare-lip and some birth-marks in an infant are due to the mother

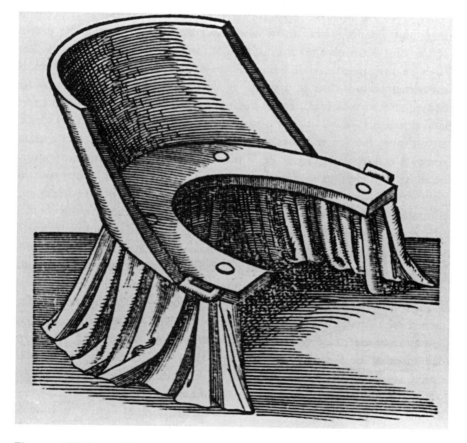

Figure 16 Birth-stool (courtesy of the Royal College of Obstetricians and Gynaecologists)

being frightened during pregnancy. For the conduct of labour he recommended a birth-stool (Fig. 16). The midwife is advised to stretch the neck of the womb to facilitate delivery of the child,[10] the usual practice at the time and one which must have been responsible for many maternal deaths from infection. After the birth of the child she was required to insert her hand into the womb and extract the placenta, another dangerous procedure, though necessary if spontaneous expulsion fails to occur. Fifteen different forms of malpresentation of the fetus are described and illustrated, with advice to the midwife on what to do in each case. As a last resort, if the child cannot be delivered alive, a surgeon should be called in to destroy and extract the child with instruments.[11]

Mrs Jane Sharp was the first English midwife to publish a book on midwifery, *The Midwives Book* (1671). The book describes the anatomy of male and female genital organs and states that 'conception is the proper action of the womb after fruitful seed is cast into it by both sexes.'[12] The signs of pregnancy are described as we know them today: cessation of menstrual periods, loss of appetite and sometimes vomiting, longing for particular items of food, and swelling of the breasts.[13] Her conduct of labour was also more modern, because less meddlesome, than was usual at the time; fetal membranes were not ruptured prematurely and manual removal of the placenta was performed only if it did not emerge spontaneously.[14] In addition to treatment of the complications of labour and the puerperium Mrs Sharp proffered advice on the choice of wet-nurse and the treatment of diseases of young children. Breast-feeding by the mother was recommended but, if a wet-nurse is required, she should be well-formed and healthy; an interesting factor in Jane Sharp's choice is that 'a female Child must suck the breasts of a Nurse that had a Girl the last child she had, and a Boy must suck her that lately had a boy'.[15]

Percival Willughby, who practised in Derby as a family doctor and consulting man-midwife for more than forty years, was a qualified surgeon and an extra-licentiate of the College of Physicians. He trained one of his daughters to be a midwife. His *Observations in Midwifery*, describing in simple terms for midwives 150 cases he had attended between 1624 and 1672, was not published until 1863.[16] He advised that the genital passage should not be stretched and that the foetal membranes should be allowed to rupture spontaneously.[17] The placenta should be removed gently and only if it is not expelled spontaneously or after administration of drugs to promote expulsion.[18] Most mal-presentations should be manipulated so that the child can be drawn out by the feet.[19] Willughby deplores the usual crude practice of midwifery and states that it is usually safer for a woman to give birth alone than with the help of a midwife.[20]

The Chamberlens, a family of Huguenot immigrants, are the best-known man-midwives of the seventeenth century. To quote Spencer:

> As inventors of the obstetric forceps – the most beneficial of surgical instruments – the name of the Chamberlens is immortal, though its lustre is tarnished by the secrecy which they maintained in regard to the nature of their invention, and by the boasting and self-seeking of the most conspicuous members.[21]

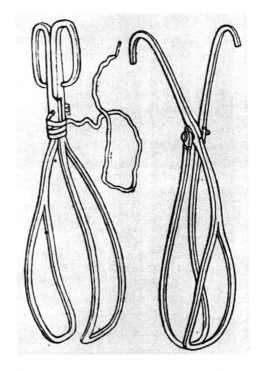

Figure 17. The Chamberlen obstetrical forceps (courtesy of the Wellcome Historical Medical Library, London).

William Chamberlen, a Huguenot refugee, settled in England in 1569, practised medicine, and died before 1596, leaving two sons, both called Peter, who practised surgery. Peter Chamberlen the elder is credited with the invention of the obstetric forceps (Fig. 17) early in the seventeenth century, but it was kept a family secret for more than 100 years. The Chamberlens were often at odds with authority. Peter the elder and his brother, Peter the younger, were often in conflict with the Barber-Surgeons' Company for not attending lectures and with the College of Physicians for practising medicine though not licensed by the College. Peter the younger's son, Peter Chamberlen III (also known as Dr Peter Chamberlen) trained at Cambridge, Heidelberg and Padua, where he graduated MD in 1619, later incorporating the degree at Oxford and

Cambridge and being elected Fellow of the College of Physicians in 1628. He tried unsuccessfully to create a Corporation of Midwives with himself as governor. In 1649 he was dismissed from the Fellowship of the College of Physicians for not attending meetings and in 1660 he was appointed physician in ordinary to King Charles II, a post later held by his son, Dr Hugh Chamberlen senior, the translator of Mauriceau's great book on midwifery (p. 66). In the preface Hugh claimed that the Chamberlens could conduct difficult labours, which no one else could do successfully, and apologised for not revealing the method,

> there being my Father and two Brothers living that practise this art, I cannot esteem it my own to dispose of, nor publish it without injury to them and think I have not been unserviceable to my country altho I do but inform them that the fore-mentioned three persons of our family and myself can serve them in these extremities with greater safety than others.[22]

The secret of the obstetric forceps was revealed only when the last of the line, Dr Hugh Chamberlen junior, died in 1728, shortly after taking out Swedish and Danish patents on the instrument.[23] A box containing what was probably the original obstetric forceps was found in 1818 under the floor of a house which had belonged to Dr Peter Chamberlen.

Obstetrical literature

Even before Rueff's *Expert Midwife*, Philip Barrough had devoted a chapter of his massive *The Method of Physick* (1617) to midwifery. This book, written in English, 'though some think this discredits the art', attributes difficult labour to weakness of the mother, weakness or deformity of the child, or narrowness of the birth passage.[24] Any presentation other than head or breech is regarded as a serious complication, as is premature rupture of the membranes. Barrough, like Soranus (p. 120), recommends early manual removal of the placenta.[25]

A chapter in William Harvey's *De generatione* (p. 87) is devoted to midwifery but is more concerned with the mechanism than with the conduct of labour. Like many other writers since the time of Hippocrates Harvey thought that the fetus plays an active part in the process. 'An easy and orderly delivery relies upon the joint endeavour of both the mother and the fetus',[26] a view discarded today. Case records are not available of Harvey's practice as a man-midwife but Willughby, who was taught by him, and others greatly admired his technique.

William Sermon, 'Doctor in Physick, one of His Majesties Physicians in Ordinary', wrote a book, *The Ladies Companion or the English Midwife* (1671) which, like Willughby, recommends the minimum of interference during labour. The midwife may attempt to enlarge the birth passage but only if the child's head is too big for it.[27] Different malpresentations (including twin pregnancies) are illustrated, with advice on how to deal with each.[28] A potion to promote expulsion of a dead child is: 'Take Oyl of Amber 15 grains, Oyl of Cinnamon two drops, Extract of Saffron three grains, Borax one scruple, mix them all together and give it in four ounces of Mugwort or Savin-water.[29]

The most detailed and accurate account to date of the structure and function of the female reproductive system, *De mulierum organis generationi inservientibus tractatus novus* (1672) was written by a Dutchman, Regnier de Graaf but not translated into English in the seventeenth century, so was available only to those who could read Latin. The best guide to obstetric practice was Dr Hugh Chamberlen's translation into English in 1673 of *Des maladies des femmes grosses et accouchées* (1668) by François Mauriceau, the leading French obstetrician of the time. According to the British surgeon, Sir D'Arcy Power, midwifery became a speciality only after publication of this book.[30]

John Pechey, who edited the works of Thomas Sydenham and wrote on many aspects of medicine, published in 1698 *The Compleat Midwives Practice Enlarged*, a book which shows little evidence of original experience but reflects the enlightened view at the end of the century that the foetal membranes should be allowed to break of their own accord and that manual removal of the placenta should be performed only when attempts to achieve spontaneous expulsion are unsuccessful.[31] The book includes a short section on diseases of children.

Pregnancy

The signs of pregnancy, as described by Jane Sharp (p. 122) were well known in the seventeenth century. Uroscopy (p. 47) was practised to diagnose not only pregnancy but also the sex of the child; this practice was discredited by the end of the century. Many people, including Sermon, believed that in pregnancy with a male child the mother's right breast and belly are larger and the right pulse stronger than the left.[32] Mauriceau stated that the sex of an unborn child cannot be predicted,[33] which was true until modern technology made it possible.

Much advice, some of it good, was available to the pregnant woman on exercise, clothing, personal hygiene and diet. Exercise was recommended but not horseback riding, which might cause miscarriage. Clothes should not be too tight. Bathing was not encouraged, especially in public baths for fear of infection.[34] Dietary advice was usually a recommendation to avoid certain foodstuffs, the veto depending on the adviser. Mauriceau thought meals should be small and frequent and constipation should be avoided but without strong purgation, which might cause abortion.[35] It was generally believed that the poor had easier labour than the rich, probably a true belief because poor women were more physically active.

Spontaneous abortion, noted by Rueff as a complication of early pregnancy, was thought to be due to weakness of the connection between fetus and womb, but could be brought on by 'dancing, riding, immoderate exercise and blowes'.[36] To prevent abortion moderate exercise and a simple diet were considered important and strong medicines were to be avoided during the first four months of pregnancy. Medicinal and mechanical means to procure abortion, such as abortifacient drugs or rupturing the fetal membranes, had been used since earliest times but, being contrary to the laws of Church and State in western Europe, are seldom mentioned in the literature.

Normal labour

The mother might be delivered on a birth-stool as recommended by Rueff (p. 121) but in England she was usually in bed, often propped up with thighs apart and knees bent. During the stage of expulsion the midwife encouraged the mother to bear down and might attempt to promote delivery by pressing down on the top of the uterus through the abdominal wall.

In the conduct even of normal labour the midwife usually followed the practice of her predecessors in considerable manual intervention. She would insert her hand, lubricated with oil or fat, into the vagina and attempt to stretch the birth canal. She might even rupture the fetal membranes, which would make labour more difficult, and after the birth of the child she would attempt to tear the placenta from the lining of the uterus before natural separation had taken place. Maternal death from infection or bleeding was common. Mauriceau wrote that a midwife should not perform manual removal of any placenta but should summon assistance from a surgeon if it was not expelled spontaneously.[37] It was usual to cut the umbilical cord between ligatures as soon as possible after the birth of the child. The infant was then cleaned, anointed with oil or butter, wrapped up tightly, and given a spoonful of wine.

Complications of labour

The commonest complication of labour, then as now, was malpresentation of the fetus and the early practice was to attempt to convert all others to a head presentation, even if this involved forcing a protruding limb back into the uterus. Such a procedure was difficult and seldom effective. Both Ambroise Paré in France and William Harvey in England recommended podalic version in these cases (changing the presentation to a breech and delivering the child by traction on the legs). In twin births it was often easier to extract the second child in this way. Percival Willughby practised and taught this technique but few midwives adopted it.

Various drugs might be administered to promote uterine contractions if these weakened during a prolonged, difficult labour; one herbal mixture contained figs, pennyroyal, mugwort, myrrh, saffron, sugar and cinnamon.[38] Saffron is a constituent of several mixtures prescribed for this purpose. If labour was unduly prolonged a surgeon or man-midwife, if available, was called in. If necessary the child was destroyed and extracted with sharp instruments, especially the crochet (a hook), which had to be handled with great care to avoid injuring the mother.[39] Caesarian section, being invariably fatal to the mother, was performed only if she had died.

When the mother's birth canal was torn some midwives or man-midwives repaired the wound by stitching the edges together but others, including Willughby, preferred to leave it open in the hope that it would make the next birth easier. The laceration was covered with poultices and protected from urine; if it extended to the anus it had to be stitched.[40] Severe bleeding before birth usually caused the death of the child and severe bleeding after birth was fatal to the mother,[41] the customary treatment was to cause further loss of blood by bleeding from an arm 'to divert the flow'.

Another grave risk was of puerperal (childbed) fever, due to infection of the womb, particularly liable to occur if the midwife's hand had been inserted into it. The treatment by venesection, purgation, and herbal mixtures was, at the best, ineffective and, at the worst, lethal. Epidemics of puerperal fever did not occur until the establishment of maternity hospitals in the eighteenth century.

Falling (prolapse) of the womb was fairly common and caused in some cases by clumsy midwifery. The treatment was to lift it back into its normal position and hold it there with a pessary.[42] Permanent surgical repair was unknown.

Puerperium

After the birth of the child a warm poultice might be applied to the mother's genital area and changed three or four times a day or it might be bathed with a herbal lotion.

Sharp recommended breast-feeding by the mother. If a woman was going to nurse her own child the breasts were to be anointed with oil of roses and vinegar. Chaps of the nipples were protected with little cups of wax.[43] Mauriceau found that some mothers must have milk drawn off 'by a lusty infant' or a glass aspirator before they could suckle their own baby.[44] Excess of milk was treated with a poultice of 'Housleek, Lettice, Poppies and Water Lillies'.[45] For inflamed breasts a cooling diet, bleeding, and a purge were recommended and local application of a cloth dipped in oil of roses with honey and water.[46]

In spite of expert advice to do so few upper-class women suckled their own children. The mother would be kept at rest in a warm, dark room for several days and fomentations, ointments, or poultices were applied to the breasts to arrest lactation while a suitable wet-nurse was found.

Gynaecology

Although gynaecology was not regarded as a medical or surgical specialty in the seventeenth century most writers on midwifery described also some diseases peculiar to women.

Menstrual disorders seem to have been the commonest. It was realised that amenorrhoea (cessation of menses) could be due to causes other than pregnancy, such as corruption of the blood, a bad constitution, weakness or, in unmarried girls, the green sickness (see below). To promote menstruation a julep might be prescribed containing mugwort, pennyroyal and cinnamon.[47] Menorrhagia (excessive menstruation) was attributed to damage to blood vessels, violent purgation, or injury; one method of treatment was to anoint the back with oils of roses, myrtles and quinces, and drink a draught of roots or leaves of comfrey in ale.[48] Another prescription was of a powder of twenty constituents, ranging from *terra sigillata* (p. 64) to water lilies.[49] Dysmenorrhoea (painful menstruation) is not described by seventeenth-century authors.

According to Rueff the cause of sterility may be 'a man-like woman or a woman-like man.[50] Other causes included tumour or inflammation of the womb and witchcraft.

Cancer of the womb was regarded as incurable but operation might be performed to remove a breast cancer if it was loose and there was no evidence of spread to other parts of the body.[51]

The green sickness (chlorosis), an iron-deficiency anaemia, was common in young unmarried women and attributed to 'the Terms stopt and from thence ill humours abound'.[52] Various herbal remedies were in use, one of which contained chicory, aniseed, damask roses, and cinnamon;[53] lacking iron they were ineffective. A better prescription was pills of steel filings in extract of wormwood.[54] Another remedy sometimes recommended was marriage.

Nursing

The development of nursing

From the earliest times until at least the mid-nineteenth century most nursing was performed at home by female members of the family. A woman with particular skill and interest in nursing the sick might help friends and relations when they were ill. In ancient Greece and Rome domestic nursing was usually performed by slaves but, although midwives and wet-nurses were common, there were no professional sick nurses. In the fourth century a widow, Fabiola, established and nursed in the first hospital for the sick (*nosocomium*) in Rome.[55]

With the spread of Christianity when monasteries and convents were established they usually had an infirmary inside the walls for treating their own sick and sometimes another outside the walls for the general public. The patients were nursed by monks or nuns, some of whom might have some knowledge of medicine, and were well cared for; their diet even included meat, which was denied to their nurses.[56]

During the First Crusade the first Christian nursing order, the Knights of St John of Jerusalem, was founded, probably in 1099, with the double purpose of defending Jerusalem and nursing pilgrims. Due to successive Islamic victories they had to move their headquarters from Jerusalem to Acre, Cyprus, Rhodes and finally Malta, but they established hospitals throughout Europe.[57] Another military order, the Teutonic Knights, founded in Jerusalem in 1128, established hospitals and employed women as well as men for nursing.[58] In the twelfth century a distinction began to be made between establishments for the sick and for the aged and indigent.

Numerous leper hospitals were provided for the sick. There were 200 such hospitals in England in the twelfth century but their function was isolation rather than treatment; the inmates were left to nurse each other.[59] By the sixteenth century leprosy was rare in Europe and most of the hospitals were abandoned, though some were used for plague patients during epidemics, even in the seventeenth century.

St Francis and St Dominic each founded three orders, one for friars, one for nuns and a secular order for men or women; many of these 'tertiaries' practised nursing.[60] The best-known regular order was the Augustinian Sisters of the *Hôtel Dieu* in Paris, established in the thirteenth century and still active today. The best-known tertiary order was also French; the *Filles de Charité* were organised by St Vincent de Paul in the seventeenth century, under the direction of a widow, Mme Le Graz, to treat the sick in their homes and provide food and prescribed medicines.[61] They also helped the Augustinian sisters in the *Hôtel Dieu* and later served in other hospitals but did not take vows as nuns, which would have hampered their nursing activities. The nurses were carefully selected, of high moral standards, and received some training in nursing.

In the sixteenth century the Brothers Hospitallers of St John of God, founded in Spain, spread through Europe and to the new colonies; they included physicians, surgeons, dentists, apothecaries and nurses.[62]

English nursing

England was less fortunate than France in the quality of its nurses and the Reformation dissolved such nursing orders as there were. With the closure of monasteries and convents, nursing was no longer available to the sick poor. In 1538 the mayor, aldermen and citizens of London petitioned King Henry VIII to reopen some hospitals; he consented and granted endowments to St Bartholomew's, St Thomas's and Bethlehem (p. 10). The charter for St Bartholomew's Hospital provided for a matron and twelve other women to make beds and 'wash and attend upon the said poor men and women there'. They catered for about 100 patients and were called sisters from monastic custom.[63] The matron was responsible for sisters and patients and the sister had to obey her. In spite of the discipline there was usually competition for vacant places.

As the population of London grew more patients had to be accommodated and a junior category of nurse was established, from which vacancies in the post of sister were filled, and helpers and watchers were employed. Hospital diet was quite good, including meat, bread, milk, butter, cheese and beer, but hospitals, as well as private houses of the period, were plagued with vermin from people, clothing and bedding.[64]

Professional nurses, other than those employed in hospitals, usually came from the lowest orders of society and were often ignorant, dirty and dishonest. During the Great Plague of London in 1665 many female servants, abandoned by their masters who had fled to the country, hired themselves to the civic authority to attend plague victims; these women were often suspected of smothering their patients with a view to stealing their possessions (p. 157).

The best nursing in England was provided by the ladies of the aristocracy and upper class housewives to their own families and dependents. These women regarded caring for the sick as one of their domestic duties and had usually inherited some traditional skills.

The low salary, long working hours, and menial tasks involved in nursing must have discouraged many women from becoming nurses in the seventeenth century and still do today. Nevertheless, since the outstanding reforms introduced by Florence Nightingale and others in the mid-nineteenth century, the profession has a higher standing in the community and has attracted women from a wider social spectrum.

CHAPTER 9

Housewives, Clergy and Quacks

MUCH MEDICAL AND SURGICAL TREATMENT In the seventeenth century was provided by men or women not legally qualified to do so. It is appropriate to distinguish the empirics, including many housewives and some clergy, who did it from a sense of duty and not for personal gain, from the quacks. The typical quack was a charlatan, who made great claims for the efficacy of his secret remedies and often great profit from the sale of them. Both empirics and quacks might use treatment prescribed by eminent physicians as well as their own, often traditional, remedies and some surgical operations were commonly left to quacks either because qualified surgeons were unwilling to take the risk or because particular quacks had developed particular skills in their performance.

Housewives

Most medical treatment and treatment of minor injuries were the responsibility of the women of the family. Although anyone might practise domestic medicine it was usually the housewife who did so and most lists of domestic remedies were written by or for housewives. Among the gentry the lady of the house would look after the servants as well as her own family. In rural districts the lady of the manor might treat villagers when they were ill. Female relatives or friends might also conduct confinements, often a much safer arrangement than submitting to the ministrations of a midwife (p. 123).

Lady Margaret Hoby

Lady Margaret Hoby, 'the earliest known British woman diarist',[1] was born in 1571 to a wealthy Yorkshire land-owner, Arthur Dakins, and his wife. She was brought up in the strictly Puritan household of the Earl of Huntingdon, where she was taught domestic skills by the Countess, and was married and widowed twice before the age of 25, when she married

Sir Thomas Hoby of Hackness in Yorkshire. She had no children and lived at Hackness, with occasional visits elsewhere, until her death in 1633.

Lady Hoby's diary from 1599 to 1603, edited by Dorothy Meads in 1930, is a record, at first daily and later intermittent, of prayers, meals and domestic affairs, including a few references to medical and surgical care of the local poor. Most early entries start: 'After privat praier', and end: 'and so to bed'. Later entries are briefer and omit going to bed.

Lady Hoby was often ill and usually treated herself, though sometimes she consulted a physician. Her care of the sick included providing medicines, dressing wounds and sores, and assisting at births. Her diary usually gives no details of treatment. 'I dressed the hand of one of our servants that was verie sore Cutt' and 'dressed a poor boyes Legge that was hurt'.[2] 'This day blakeborn [a servant] Cutt his foot with a hatchett' and the next day [I] dressed Blakebornes foott'.[3] Lady Hoby's most ambitious venture into surgery was on an infant with an imperforate anus:

> This day in the afternone, I had had a child brought . . . who had no fundement and had no passage for excrements but att the Mouth: I was ernestly intreated to Cutt the place to se if any passhage Could be made, but, although I Cutt deepe and searched, there was none to be found.[4]

The Countess of Kent

Elizabeth Grey, Countess of Kent, published in 1653 *A Choice Manuall or Rare and Select Secrets in Physick*. She quotes the source of some of her remedies, often a reputable physician, but most are not acknowledged and are presumably traditional. The Countess's prescriptions are as varied as the conditions she treated. For the falling sickness (epilepsy): 'Take the dung of a Peacock, make it into powder and give as much of it to the patient as will lie upon a shilling in Succory water fasting', and for the bloody flux (dysentery): 'Take the bone of a Gammon of Bacon and set it up an [sic] end in the middle of a Charcoal fire, and let it burn till it looks like Chalk and will burn no longer, then powder it and give the powder therof to the sick.'[5] A prescription, which can hardly have been effective, 'against the biting of a mad Dog and the rage or madness that followeth a man after he is bitten' (rabies), is as follows: 'Take the Blossomes or Floures of wild Thistles dryed in the shade, and beaten to powder, give him to drink of that powder in white Wine, half a Walnut shell full, and in thrice taking it, he shall be healed.'[6] To prepare one of several remedies for the plague:

> Take one pound of green Walnuts, half an ounce of *London* Triacle [theriac, p. 39], beaten together in a morter, and with a little *Carduus*, or some such water, vapour it over the fire till it come to an Electuary, keep this in a pot and take as much as a Walnut, it is good to cure a Feaver, Plague and any infection.[7]

Medicines were not all to be taken by mouth. To take away a headache: 'Take the best Sallade oyle, and the glasse half full with the tips of Poppy floures which groweth in the Corn, set this in the Sun a fortnight, and so keep it all the year and anoint the Temples of your head with it'.[8] For a cough: 'Take Sallade oyle, *Aqua vitae*, and Sack, of each an equall quantity, heat them altogether, and before the fire rub the soles of your feet with it.'[9] Sometimes oral and other remedies were combined. For a difficult labour: 'Take a date stone, beat it into powder, let the woman drink it with Wine, then take Polipody and emplaister it to her feet, and the Child will come whether it be quick or dead'.[10] It is difficult to see how this treatment can have been effective.

More success may have followed the treatment of Emeroids (piles). 'Take Hops and Vinegar, fry them together and put it into a little bag, and lay it as hot as may be endured to the Fundament, divers bags one after another, and let one continue at it.'[11] An ointment for wounds was prepared by sterilising at least some of the constituents by boiling, although the value of this procedure would not be recognised for another two centuries. The prescription reads as follows:

> Take Rosin and Wax of each half a pound, of Deer Suet and Frankincense of each one quarter of a pound, of Mastick in powder one ounce, boil all these in a pint of white Wine half an houre with a soft fire and stir it in the boyling that it run not over, then take it from the fire and put thereto an ounce of Camphire in pouder, when it is almost cold put thereto one quarter of a pound of Turpentine, after all these be mingled together then put it into white Wine and wash it as you wash butter, and then as it cools make it up into rouls [rolls].[12]

The Manuall contains many other prescriptions for a great variety of diseases.

Mary Doggett

Mary Doggett, wife of Thomas Doggett, the 'Player', wrote a *Book of Receipts* (1682), the manuscript of which is in the British Library but has never been published. It is a strange mixture of recipes for cooking and prescriptions for medicines. Among the former are instructions 'To preserve Cherrys', 'To make Lemon-pudings or Cheese-cakes', 'To make Little Cakes', 'To make a Pye', and 'To Boyle a Legg of Mutton or a Rump of Beefe'. Among the latter are prescriptions for ailments as diverse as bladder stone, jaundice, scurvy, rickets, gout, colic and plague.

The instructions are detailed, e.g.

> How to make Cordiall Water. Take a quart of running water, put to it a pound of Loafe Sugar mix them together and lett run 3 times through a Cotten bag, then put to it a pint of Cinnamon water, a pint of Damask rose water powre all these things through a Cotten bag 3 times then put in 3 pints of Aqua Vitae, then powre it 3 times more through ye Cotten bag, then glass it up close for your use.[13]

A potion for scurvy, which would be effective though unnecessarily complex, was:

> Take Scurvy grass bruised 3 pound hors Radish Roots cut and bruised one part infused in an equall part of Sack or white wine all night so that ye wine cover them a finger bredth, Let them be stopt close cast them into a cold still a [*sic*] water from thence you may add a quart of Juice of Oranges or a Third proportion of it or to this quantity spoken off add 12 oranges cut them into very thin slices so that ye Juce and Kind Joyne to be taken a wine glass full 2 or 3 times a day.[14]

Another useful and simpler prescription was a preparation of iron, which would have helped some cases of anaemia, though Mary Doggett does not specify its use:

> To make Steele Wine. Take fileings of Steele, which you may have at ye needle makers wash it in water to cleanse it from dust, which may have accidentally fallen in, then wet it with vinegar upon a Stone 3 or 4 days together. Spread it abroad and lett it dry till it be all over Red with rust, ye more rusty and old the better, then pound it and scearch it very fine [pick it over carefully to remove foreign matter] and put 2 pound of it into a Gallon of any wine either Sack white or Renish according to the constitution of ye patient but Renish is

ye best being not so hot as canary nor so raw as white wine. Shake it every day for a week together.[15]

Lady Catherine Sedley

More is known about Lady Catherine Sedley than about the Countess of Kent or Mary Doggett. She was the daughter of the Earl of Rivers and married Sir Charles Sedley, a companion of King Charles II, in 1657. Their only child, Catherine, was a mistress of King James II, who made her Countess of Dorchester.

Lady Sedley's receipt book, dated 1686 but never published, contains 140 recipes and prescriptions, 16 culinary and the rest medical or cosmetic.[16] Several prescriptions are provided for each of the following major ailments: dropsy, palsy, bladder stone, ague, plague, smallpox, scurvy, jaundice, rickets, convulsions and consumption. Minor ailments for which treatment is prescribed include piles, incontinence of urine, cough, nose-bleeding, headache, constipation, worms and toothache. Some of the prescriptions are attributed to particular individuals, not necessarily physicians, e.g. Sir Kellam [sic] Digby's *aqua mirabilis*, Sir Thomas Weatherly's diet drink for the gout, Dr Jacob of Canterbury's medicine for the stone, and Dr King's receipt for 'the griping of the guts'. This last prescription reveals the current belief that drugs could be absorbed through the umbilicus. 'Take a penny loaf and slitt it and toast it and spread it over with venice treakle, and dip it in sack boyled with cloves, cinnamon, and nutmegg; tye it in a cloath, and lay it hot to the navel'.[17] Other prescriptions, presumably traditional, include 'A Receipt for the Convulsion fitts: Take a quart of white wine, put it into a good handfull of Cowslips leaves, boyle away a third part, then take it of the fire and let it Stand till the next day, then Strayne it, and so drink it till all be done.[18]

> 'A Receipt for Piels [sic] that never faileth' is Take four ounces of white lead, the like quantity of white frankincense, and sift them through a Tiffany [muslin gauze] and mix them with good honey till they be as thick as to spread for a plaister, then spread it on a linen cloath, and apply it to the place as warm as you can endure it.[19]

The prescription for difficult labour resembles that of the Countess of Kent (see above): 'Take Bittonye and Date Stones in powder and drink it and she shall be delivered anon.'[20] An example of a cosmetic prescription is 'a receipt for a red face':

Take the Juice of Southernwood one large spoonfull put it into a pint of strong Ale or half a pint of Sacke drinke this by six of the Clock in the morninge fastinge, abstain from eatinge or drinkinge untill Tenn then take Southernwood and put a little vinegar to it and eat it with bread and butter as sage and at Twelve you may go to diner, this is to be observed for tenn dayes together.[21]

Lady Ranelagh

Another receipt book in manuscript, undated but including prescriptions by Sir Kenelm Digby (p. 142), was written by Lady Ranelagh, daughter of the Earl of Cork. As with other receipt books of the period most of the prescriptions are unlikely to have had any beneficial effect. Fever might be treated by an oral preparation, herbs and snails crushed in a mortar, added to milk, and allowed to stand for two weeks, or by applying the bones of a pickled herring to the soles of the feet.[22] For the biting of a mad dog: Leaves of Varsine, plantine and rue in treacle and wine to drink and apply to the wound. 'This has often been proved and has never failed any'.[23] Medicines which should have been effective include a purge of rhubarb and syrup of roses in chicken broth and, 'to stay loosnesse [diarrhoea] take terra lemna [*terra sigillata* p. 64] and fine red bole [clay] scrape them and take as much of each as will lye on a groat in conserve of Roses.'[24]

Medical writers on domestic medicine

Leonard Sowerby wrote for the benefit of housewives *The Ladies Dispensatory* (1652), 'consisting of pure Elementary Simples, not . . . a hodge podge of sophisticated Drugs . . . one appugning the other'. Although complex mixtures were avoided the simple remedies were strange and varied. Three of the treatments prescribed for epilepsy were: 'The Liver of an Asse rosted, eaten fasting', 'Gall of a Tortoise put in the nose' and 'Root of Sea-holly drunke in water'.[25] 'Snayles which stick to bryers and bushes eaten'[26] were prescribed to cause vomiting and would probably do so. 'To void the stone of the Bladder . . . Mice dung taken in honied wine with Frank-incense'[27] can hardly have been effective and 'pestilentiall Feavers' would not have been relieved by Sweet Chervill 'drunk every day twice or thrice a day'.[28] The most succinct treatment is of ulcers: 'Cobwebs applied'.[29]

Gideon Harvey, another writer who encouraged domestic medicine, was physician in ordinary to King Charles II. In *The Family-Physician and the*

House-Apothecary (1676), he provided 'Instructions, whereby to prepare at your own Houses all kinds of necessary Medicines that are prepared by *Apothecaries* or prescribed by *Physicians*.' Harvey wrote: 'That it's plainly made to appear, that in preparing Medicines thus at your own Houses, that it's not onely a far safer way, but you shall also save Nineteen shillings in Twenty, comparing it with the extravagant Rates of many *Apothecaries*.'[30] 'This treatise', he says, 'selects from the London Dispensatory a small number of commonly used medicines which can be prepared at home.' It teaches how to compound them and gives the price of the ingredients. Methods of preparation are described for a whole range of oral preparations, for suppositories and enemas, for ointments and plasters, and for eye lotions. Most are simple, such as senna and fennel in ale as a purgative[31] and barley water with lemon and sugar for fever.[32] Gideon Harvey was a competent physician but a thorn in the flesh of the College of Physicians and the Society of Apothecaries, both of which preferred to keep their remedies secret and expensive. He wrote: 'More owe their Deaths to Physicians than are pretendedly cured by them.'[33]

Clergy

Care of the sick was no longer an official duty of the Church, as it had been in the Middle Ages, but some clergymen practised medicine, without the approval of the College of Physicians but usually without active interference from that body. A divinity student, studying for his first degree at Oxford or Cambridge, could learn as much about medicine as a medical student at that stage and, during the religious disturbances of the early Stuart period, many may have decided to follow the more secure profession of medicine. Richard Napier and John Ward were two ordained clergymen who practised medicine without satisfying the legal requirements; they may be distinguished from quacks because their motive was not financial gain, although both became wealthy.

Richard Napier

Of Scottish descent, Richard Napier was born in 1559 and studied theology at Oxford, graduating BA in 1584 and MA in 1586. Thereafter most of his long life, until his death in 1634, was spent as rector of Great Linton, a small village in Buckinghamshire, where he employed curates to perform his church duties, while he devoted his time to the mentally and physically ill. His fame as a healer spread, especially in Buckinghamshire and the adjacent counties of Northamptonshire and Bedfordshire, and he treated tens of thousands of patients of all ranks of society. He charged small fees and gave generously to the poor.[34]

As expressed by Michael MacDonald, who has analysed Napier's case records: 'Napier lived during the last era in which a prestigious medical practitioner could reconcile his beliefs in astrology, magic, religion and science'.[35] He studied the horoscope of each patient as an aid to diagnosis and treatment and, as recorded by Aubrey in his *Brief Lives*, he conversed with the archangel Raphael, who would sometimes tell him whether the patient was curable or incurable.[36] He often prayed with his patients. Napier also studied alchemy and prepared some of his own chemical remedies.[37]

Most of Napier's patients had physical maladies and received conventional medical treatment; these and the mentally ill (p. 69) might be subjected to purges, enemas and bleeding, as well as to sundry medicaments. In addition to his own remedies Napier employed drugs recommended in the *Pharmacopoea Londinensis* and traditional folk remedies. He also prepared amulets and performed exorcisms for some mental and some other patients.[38] This last treatment was not without danger to the healer because the punishment for sorcery was death.

John Ward

John Ward was born in 1629 in Spratton, Northamptonshire, the son of a rural vicar. He graduated BA and MA Oxon, in 1649 and 1652 respectively, was ordained in 1661, and became vicar of Stratford-on-Avon in 1662, an appointment which he held until his death in 1681. He never married.

At Oxford Ward studied medical subjects and associated with Thomas Willis (p. 17) and Robert Boyle (p. 86). His fellow-students included Richard Lower (p. 77). He learnt botany from Jacob Bobart, keeper of the herb garden, and chemistry from Peter Stahl, who worked with Boyle. From Stratford, Ward frequently visited London and Oxford to keep in touch with physicians, botanists and chemists. 'Even while serving as the incumbent at Stratford-on-Avon his diaries reflected a greater concern for his parishioners' bodies than for their souls.'[39] Although he acted for some time as an informal apprentice to a physician, William Conyers, Ward never acquired any medical qualification.

The sixteen diaries, starting in 1663 and briefer after 1670, contain a mixture of medicine, theology and history, including accounts of medical and surgical cases, outlines of sermons, and comments on current events. His treatment was the conventional medicine of the day, as practised by leading physicians, and lacked the elements of superstition and magic of Richard Napier earlier in the century. Blood-letting, he said, is futile 'unless it can be supposed that only the corrupt blood comes forth.'[40] 'Faintings in a feavour, or after letting blood, are dangerous. Mr Waulford thrice let blood and dead.'[41] Ward's treatment was conservative, believing, as he did, 'Some medicines will be sure to weaken the body but not the disease.'[42] Even for plague: 'You doe nothing in the plague unless you sweat twice a day, and when the malignitie is collected into one bubo the best way is to pultis [poultice] and ripen itt [sic] that itt may break and so dissolve itt.'[43]

Ward quotes some interesting remarks by other practitioners. 'Nick Culpeper says that a physitian without astrology is like a pudden without fat.'[44] 'Physick, says Dr Sydenham, is not to be learned by going to universities but hee is for taking apprentices and says one had as good send a man to Oxford to learn shoemaking as practising physick.'[45] Ward comments on treatment by some physicians and surgeons and by some well-known quacks of the period, including Sir Kenelm Digby (p. 141) and Valentine Greatrakes (p. 143).

Quacks

Quack doctors were common in England from the fourteenth century and very numerous under James I, when the London magistrates were ordered to bring them to trial before the College of Physicians, which could fine or imprison them. Most quacks sold secret remedies, but quite respectable physicians did this in the seventeenth century. Many employed astrology in their practice, even towards the end of the century when most physicians had abandoned it. The least reputable quacks were the travelling mountebanks (p. 9), who sold their medicines from a portable stage and were usually accompanied by a clown and sometimes by a monkey (Fig. 18). The function of the clown (or Merry Andrew, so-called after the witty

Figure 18. A mountebank and his clown. From a 17th-century engraving.

Dr Andrew Boorde, physician to King Henry VIII) was to entertain the audience and put them in good humour to purchase the quack's nostrums.

Some surgical operations were mostly performed by quacks, often in public on the village green; these included the operations for harelip and wryneck.[46] Other operations commonly performed by quacks, who had acquired with practice particular skill in the technique, were extracting teeth, couching for cataract (p. 103) and cutting for the stone (p. 106).

Some quacks, although untrained, obtained a College licence or a royal licence but most practised illegally. To get a licence testimonials were required from accredited physicians or 'persons of quality', stating that the applicant was well known as a practitioner of medicine and surgery. The quack, if a mountebank, required permission from the governing body of each town where he wanted to erect his stage.[47]

Sir Kenelm Digby

Kenelm Digby was born in 1603, the son of Edward Digby, a Roman Catholic hanged for his participation in Guy Fawkes's gunpowder plot. He studied at Oxford, became a successful privateer in the Aegean Sea at the age of 24 and, on his return to England, practised medicine and surgery among many other activities. His *Observations* on Sir Thomas Browne's *Religio medici* (p. 32) were largely responsible for its immediate popularity on publication. A favourite at the court of King Charles I, by whom he was knighted, he was imprisoned by the Puritan parliament early in the First Civil War but released in 1643. He then went to Paris to continue his studies, returning to England after the Restoration. He was well received at the court of King Charles II, whose support enabled him to defy the veto of the College of Physicians on unauthorised medical practice, and was an early member of the Royal Society.

Digby is best known for his 'weapon salve' or 'sympathetic powder', which was applied not to the wound but to the weapon which had caused it, with intent to heal the wound. It could be applied for the same purpose to any object soaked in the victim's blood.[48] The idea of a weapon salve derives from Paracelsus, and Digby claimed to have learnt the secret from a Carmelite monk and to be the only person in England who knew it. In 1657 he impressed a group of French scientists at Montpellier with a case report of its efficacy.[49] The powder was probably copper sulphate.[50] Since the wound was merely washed with clean water and covered with clean dressings healing was usually better when the various ointments and powders in use at the time were applied to the weapon instead of to the wound.

Digby was a man of many interests and a prolific writer. Influenced by Descartes and Locke he produced in 1644 *Two Treatises*, one on *The Nature of Bodies* and the other on *The Nature of Mans Soule*. In the former he dabbled in embryology, in the latter in theology. He was a practising Roman Catholic, which accounts for his imprisonment and exile under the Commonwealth. He also wrote a textbook of medicine, *Choice and Experimental Receipts in Physick and Chirurgery* (1688), in which remedies are prescribed for sundry ailments and the methods of preparing them are described. Most are simple; e.g. for dropsy, cloves of garlic followed by wormwood ale;[51] for the falling sickness peony roots applied to the soles of the feet;[52] to arrest bleeding a plaster made from moss growing on a dead man's skull, mixed with mastick and tragacanth and steeped in plantain and rose water; for nose-bleeding the plaster is applied to the forehead; for the 'bloody-flux' to the navel.[53] For the king's evil 'a plaster of snails and parsley is applied to the sores'. *Aqua mirabilis*, a panacea for venereal disease, plague, dropsy and palsy, contained antimony, oil of tartar, dried horse-dung, and salt of coral.[55] Another plague remedy recommended was the traditional panacea, mithridate (p. 40). These medicines can hardly have had any beneficial effect but are similar to the prescriptions of leading physicians of the time.

Valentine Greatrakes

Valentine Greatrakes (or Greatraks), the 'stroker', was another famous quack of the seventeenth century. He was born in Ireland in 1629, studied classics and divinity in England, served in Cromwell's army in Ireland, and became a government official in Cork. He then felt endowed with the gift of healing, which he practised, often charging no fee.[56] From 1662 to 1665 he was practising in London and was employed by King Charles II, who protected him from the College of Physicians.[57] In 1666 he returned to his family estate at Affane, near Dublin, where he continued to treat the patients who came to him and where he died in 1683. Greatrakes believed he had power to cure many ailments, including the king's evil, by stroking or by the mere laying on of hands. He also performed minor surgery. Like most quacks he advertised widely, quoting many testimonials from distinguished people; many of these he wrote himself.[58] In a book entitled *A Brief Account of Mr Valentine Greatrakes and Divers of the Strange Cures by him lately performed* (1666) there are fifty-one pages of testimonials.

Cornelius Tilburg

Cornelius à Tilbourne, who later called himself Tilburg, was one of the best known of the immigrant quacks who practised in London after the Restoration. He was favoured by Charles II, who appointed him a physician in ordinary and later by William III, whose influence failed to protect him from the College of Physicians, which successfully prosecuted him in 1693 for practising medicine without a licence.[59] His chief nostrum was Orvietan, a secret preparation claimed as an antidote for poisons, but he also claimed to cure blindness, deafness, bladder or kidney stone and many other ailments. In a bill he advertised himself as 'High German Doctor or Physician, Oculist, Chirurgeon and Rupture Master'. Sometimes he advertised: 'No cure, No money'.[60] The date of his death is not known.

William Salmon

William Salmon, born in England in 1644, began his professional career as assistant to a mountebank, lived for some time in New England, and then settled in London, where he practised medicine and astrology.[61] He sold many medicines, including an 'Elixir of Life', 'Family Pills', and an antidote against plague. He published in English *Synopsis medicinae or a Compendium of Astrological, Galenical and Chymical Physick* (1671) as well as a book of astrological predictions, the *London Almanack* (1684), which was a precursor of *Old Moore's Almanack*, and books on theology, botany and anatomy. His extensive library of more than 3000 volumes contained important works in all these fields and was sold by auction after his death in 1713.[62]

John Case

John Case was born at Lyme Regis in Dorsetshire about 1660 and went to London at about the age of 15 to make his living as a writer. Finding this career unremunerative he began to practise astrology and medicine and advertised his services, sometimes in verse:

> Dear Friends let your disease be what God will,
> Pray to him for a cure, Try Cases's Skill;
> Who may be such an healing instrument,
> As will cure you to your Heart's content.
> His medicines are cheap and truly good,
> Being full as safe as your daily food,
> Case, he can do what may be done, by
> Either Physick or true Astrology.[63]

His nostrums included: 'Mundus Sanitatus, the operations of which are the wonder of the world, price 2s 6d., very proper, The Pilula Cathartic, the True Medicarem Universale, Gutta Stipitica Miraculum Mundi, the world's wonder for inward wounds, Liquor Diuretica and Analepticus, and the cordial draught or wonderful Elixir'.[64] The poor might get advice for nothing but were required to pay for the medicine prescribed.

It is reported that Case met the eminent physician, John Radcliffe, at a convivial evening and Radcliffe gave a toast: 'Here's to all the fools, your patients, brother Case.' 'I thank you, good brother,' replied Case, 'Let me have all the fools and you are heartily welcome to the rest of the practise.'[65]

The persistence of quackery

Quackery was at least as prevalent in the eighteenth as in the seventeenth century and persists today although, since the Medical Registration Act of 1858, the distinction is clearly drawn between a 'registered medical practitioner' and a quack. Although a registered doctor has had conventional training he is not required to practise conventional medicine and may legally practise homeopathy, osteopathy or any other 'alternative' form of medicine provided he conforms to the requirements of the Act. He is debarred from advertising and from associating professionally with an unqualified practitioner.

Some qualified doctors, such as John Pechey in the seventeenth century and William Read, who was knighted by Queen Anne in the eighteenth, impaired their professional standing by advertising and by making unreasonable claims for the success of their treatment. Anderson's Scots Pills, the secret remedy of a seventeenth-century physician, Dr Patrick Anderson, were still on sale in London in the twentieth century; they are a purgative compound of aloes, jalap, and oil of aniseed.[66]

Some quacks died in poverty; others became very rich. The success of quackery depends on the fact that most patients recover from most diseases without, or in spite of, treatment; the last treatment to be applied gets credit for the recovery. Modern medicine has effective remedies for many diseases, though many of them are more dangerous than the less effective treatment applied in the past. Most conventional medical treatment in the seventeenth century can have done little good and the treatment provided by quacks was no less effective and probably no more harmful.

CHAPTER 10

Infectious Diseases

T HERE CAN BE LITTLE DOUBT that most human illness in the seventeenth century, as in the twentieth, was due to infection by micro-organisms; in the seventeenth century, though not in the twentieth because of advances in medicine, infection would also be the commonest cause of death. A wide range of micro-organisms can cause disease in man and they can be transferred from one individual to another in infected breath, by direct contact with patient or fomites (clothing or other objects with which the patient has been in close contact), by ingesting infected food or water, by sexual intercourse, or by transmission by insects from another infected human being or from an infected animal.

Infectious disease may be very acute (plague), very chronic (leprosy), or intermediate between these extremes. Although their causation by micro-organisms was not appreciated until the work of Louis Pasteur in the nineteenth century, plague and leprosy had been regarded from very early times as transmissible diseases and attempts were made to limit their spread by segregation and avoidance of those suffering from the disease. By these means leprosy had been virtually eliminated from England by the seventeenth century.

Most acute infections are accompanied by a rise in body temperature (pyrexia), which may be sustained or intermittent and are called fevers. Some fevers have other characteristic features, which aid recognition, but others can only be classified, even today, as 'pyrexia of unknown origin' (P. U. O). In his classic *Methodus curandi febres* (p. 27) Thomas Sydenham distinguished continued from intermittent fevers and identified two febrile diseases, smallpox and plague.

The severity of an infectious disease fluctuates with the virulence of the infecting organism, the resistance of the patient to infection, environmental factors, and (especially in the twentieth century) the efficacy of treatment. The disease may be fairly constant in incidence in particular regions (endemic) or subject to sudden outbreaks of varying severity and duration (epidemic).

Endemic Diseases

Malaria

Malaria (ague) is an endemic disease restricted to marshy or other areas where stagnant water permits the breeding of the anopheline mosquitos which carry the disease from man to man. Although the concept of individual diseases as separate entities is relatively modern, bouts of malarial fever are so typical that they can be recognised in the works of Hippocrates.[1] The tertian ague described by Sydenham (p. 53) is due to infection with one species of Plasmodium (*P. vivax*) and the quartan ague is caused by another species (*P. malariae*). That transmission of the disease is by mosquitos was discovered only in 1898 by Sir Ronald Ross[2] and modern methods of malaria control by local destruction of mosquito larvae date from 1902, but effective treatment of individual patients was possible in England in the late seventeenth century with the powdered bark of the Cinchona tree, which was brought from Peru to Spain by Jesuit missionaries about 1640 and reached England about 1665.[3] The active principle in the bark ('Peruvian bark', 'Jesuit's bark') is quinine, which destroys the plasmodium in the blood. Both Sydenham and Willis prescribed the powdered bark for ague but it was brought to public notice by an apothecary, Robert Tabor, who cured King Charles II of ague with it after the royal physicians had refused to prescribe it, and was knighted and thereafter protected by the King from prosecution by the College of Physicians as an unqualified practitioner of medicine.[4]

Since Peruvian bark was scarce and expensive, and because there was some opposition to its use because of its association with Jesuits, there were numerous ineffective prescriptions for the treatment of ague. Mary Doggett recommended: 'Take feverfew and sage and bruise them half a pennyworth of Pepper. One little spoonful of Chinny [chimney] Soot and ye white of an egg mingle them together and lay it to ye wrist.'[5] The prescription of the Countess of Kent was:

> Take the inner bark of a Walnut tree, a good quantity, boyl it in beer until the beer look black, and then take a good draught and put it

into a pot, then take six spoonfuls of Sallet [salad] Oyle for an extreme Ague, brew it too and fro in two pots, then drinke it.[6]

Leonard Sowerby recommended for tertian ague 'a spider bruised in a cloth, spread upon linnen and applied to the fore-head or Temples' and for quartan ague 'wild Rue drunk in wine'.[7] Most physicians were agreed that excessive bleeding or purging should be avoided in this condition.

In the seventeenth century malaria was common in the Fen country, around Oxford, and also in London, where the mosquitos could breed in the stagnant water of ditches and in ponds and marshes near the city. Public health measures and effective treatment have now virtually eliminated it from England, though it is still the commonest cause of death in some Eastern countries.

Venereal diseases

The French pox (syphilis) was not reported in England before 1503[8] but was of epidemic intensity in the sixteenth century; by the seventeenth it had settled to endemic proportions, though still widely distributed. Ever since 1629, when the London Bills of Mortality first included causes of death other than plague, one of these causes was the French pox; the annual total sometimes approached 100 and was almost certainly an under-estimate. Graunt believed that many deaths from syphilis were recorded as due to some other cause, such as consumption, to avoid embarrassment to the family because of the disreputable nature of the disease.[9]

Syphilis and gonorrhoea are both transmitted by sexual intercourse, and gonorrhoea, an acute purulent infection of the urethra, was widely regarded as the first stage of syphilis because, when both diseases are transmitted simultaneously, its symptoms are the first to appear. Thomas Sydenham did not make this mistake and gave a very clear description of the onset and course of syphilis (p. 58). He treated gonorrhoea, though he did not recognise it as a disease entity, by purgation, and syphilis by the application of mercury ointment, the most effective treatment at the time, though only in toxic doses (p. 63). Barrough described the symptoms of mercury poisoning, which include loss of teeth and erosion of bones.[10] The other popular treatment was oral administration of a decoction of guaiac bark (p. 43), alone or mixed with herbs. Bruel used this and also applied a mixture of guaiac and theriac or mercury ointment to the ulcers, which are a common feature of the disease; he also prescribed numerous herbal potions, draughts and pills.[11] The surgeon, Joseph Binns, gave mercury by mouth and regulated the dosage by the side effects, which include diarrhoea and salivation;[12] he also prescribed other remedies, such as 'an apparent Cure for the French disease', which included sarsaparilla, guaiacum and mithridate in wine and beer.[13]

Although mercury might relieve the symptoms of syphilis there was no cure for the disease until the discovery of the organic arsenical preparation, salvarsan in 1910, later displaced by neosalvarsan and then by penicillin.

Tuberculosis

Tuberculosis is infection with a mycobacterium (usually *M. tuberculosis*), discovered by Robert Koch in 1882.[14] It is transferred directly from man to man, usually expelled from the lung of an affected person by coughing or spitting and usually affecting the lung of the victim, though any organ may be infected. Tubercles form at the site of infection and may break down; in the lung this leads to formation of cavities (consumption, phthisis), with pus and sometimes blood in the sputum. The infection may cause an acute fever but is more often chronic and, unlike syphilis, does not necessarily progress if untreated; it is more likely to do so if the individual's resistance is undermined by malnutrition or by some other disease and it is most likely to spread in crowded and insanitary housing conditions. Given favourable conditions many people recover from an initial infection but once destruction of lung tissue is advanced there is no recovery. Thomas Willis described phthisis as 'pining away of the whole body because of an ulcer in the lungs'[15] and John Symcotts gives an excellent description of a fatal case (p. 30).

Phthisis was recognised by Hippocrates as a prolonged and usually fatal disease.[16] It was prevalent in England in the late Middle Ages[17] and in Tudor times.[18] 'Consumption and cough' ranked above plague as causes of death in London in the twenty years prior to 1661.[19] Thomas Sydenham describes a 'pleurisy', which was almost certainly phthisis, although this is not the only cause of pleurisy. He prescribed venesection, as for other fevers, and a number of herbal mixtures, of which the following is an example: 'Take of the Water of red Poppies four Ounces; of Sal Prunella one Dram; of Syrup of Violets one Ounce; mingle them and make a Draught'.[20] Several of Sir Theodore de Mayerne's aristocratic patients suffered from consumption and one of his prescriptions was a strange mixture of animal and plant constituents (p. 20).

Preventive vaccination against tuberculosis has been practised with varying success since 1924 and effective drug therapy, available since mid-twentieth century, has greatly reduced the ravages of the disease in England but it is still a major cause of illness and death in more primitive communities.

The king's evil (scrofula, tuberculosis of lymph nodes in the neck), commonly caused by the bovine species of mycobacterium (*M. bovis*) and transmitted in milk, was widely believed to be curable by the monarch's touch. Both the sceptical Sir Thomas Browne, in *Pseudoxia epidemica* (1646), and the even more sceptical James Primrose, in *The Errours of the People in Physick* (1651), expressed this belief and Thomas Sydenham accepted it. Richard Wiseman (p. 113) described the condition and stated that the kings of England, at least since Edward the Confessor, had the power of miraculous cure of the condition.[21] Nevertheless, Wiseman prescribed medical treatment and sometimes excised the infected glands. He also noted that a similar condition of the tonsils could be cured by excision or cautery.[22]

Tuberculosis of other organs was not recognised in the seventeenth century, though evidence of tuberculosis of the spine dates from as long ago as 3400 BC in an Egyptian mummy.[23] Soft organs would be infected too but have not been preserved.

Epidemic Diseases

The most devastating disease of the seventeenth century was plague. Other epidemics were usually more localised and had a lower mortality and many were more difficult to diagnose. In a Bill of Mortality for London during the plague epidemic of 1665 (Fig. 19) there were 4237 deaths from plague, 166 from 'spotted fever' (typhus) and 11 from 'flox and small-pox' but the 348 recorded simply as 'feaver' must include other epidemic diseases and it is probable that some 'chrisomes' (new-born), 'infants' and 'aged' died of an acute infection. One wonders why 111 people in this week died of 'teeth', to what terror the 'frighted' were exposed, and what caused 'suddenly'.

The Diseases and Casualties this Week.

Imposthume	—	8
Infants	—	22
Kingsevil	—	4
Lethargy	—	1
Livergrown	—	1
Meagrome	—	1
Palsie	—	1
Plague	—	4237
Purples	—	2
Quinsie	—	5
Rickets	—	23
Rising of the Lights	—	18
Rupture	—	1
Scurvy	—	3
Shingles	—	1
Spotted Feaver	—	166
Stilborn	—	4
Stone	—	2
Stopping of the stomach	—	17
Strangury	—	3
Suddenly	—	2
Surfeit	—	74
Teeth	—	111
Thrush	—	6
Tissick	—	9
Ulcer	—	1
Vomiting	—	10
Winde	—	4
Wormes	—	20

Abortive	4
Aged	45
Bleeding	1
Broken legge	1
Broke her scull by a fall in the street at St. Mary Wool-church	1
Childbed	28
Chrisomes	9
Consumption	126
Convulsion	89
Cough	1
Dropsie	53
Feaver	348
Flox and Small-pox	11
Flux	1
Frighted	2
Gowt	1
Grief	3
Griping in the Guts	79
Head-mould-shot	1
Jaundies	7

Christned	Males — 90			
	Females — 81			
	In all — 171			
Buried	Males — 2777		Plague — 4237	
	Females — 2791			
	In all — 5568			

Increased in the Burials this Week ———— 249
Parishes clear of the Plague ——— 27   Parishes Infected ——— 103

The Assize of Bread set forth by Order of the Lord Maior and Cours of Aldermen A penny Wheaten Loaf to contain Nine Ounces and a half, and three half-penny White Loaves the like weight.

Figure 19. London Bill of Mortality for the week 16–22 August 1665 (courtesy of the London Library)

Plague

An understanding of the nature of plague had to await the development of bacteriology in the latter half of the nineteenth century and the discovery of the causative organism in 1894 by a French and a Japanese scientist independently and almost simultaneously during an epidemic of plague in Hong Kong.[24,25] Plague is a specific infectious disease caused by the plague bacillus (*Yersinia pestis*). The illness takes the form of an acute fever, which may be rapidly fatal before characteristic symptoms appear (septicaemic plague) or may cause swelling and suppuration of superficial lymph nodes. These typical swellings are called buboes so the common form of the disease is called bubonic plague. Buboes usually occur in the neck, armpit or groin; if they break down and suppurate the patient may recover. Carbuncles are also common and a particularly unfavourable sign is 'tokens', red or purple spots due to bleeding into the skin, which foretell death within a few hours.

Plague is primarily a disease of rodents, especially the black rat (*Rattus rattus*), and is transmitted from one rat to another by the rat flea, (commonly *Xenopsylla cheopis* in the tropics and *Ceratophyllus fasciatus* in temperate climates).[26] An epizootic among rats kills so many that the fleas turn their attention to the less attractive human host. Plague is usually conveyed to the human victim by a 'blocked' flea, one whose proventriculus (gizzard) is so blocked with plague bacilli that it can no longer ingest blood; on attempting to do so it regurgitates blood and plague bacilli into the wound.[27] Plague affects the lungs as well as other organs and may be transmitted to new victims in infected breath; the disease so acquired affects first the lungs (pneumonic plague) and is rapidly fatal. As the epidemic develops the plague bacillus tends to become more virulent, septicaemic or pneumonic plague becomes commoner, and many patients die before buboes or other characteristic signs of plague appear. Not everyone infected with plague dies and the survivors have some immunity against further attacks so the epidemic is ultimately self-limiting, though it may last for more than a year and cause widespread mortality. Since the rat flea moves and reproduces much more actively in warm than in cold weather epidemics of plague are usually seasonal, reaching their height in summer or early autumn and dormant during the winter.

Early attempts to limit the spread of a plague epidemic were based on segregation and avoidance of plague patients. For those who could afford to leave a stricken area the most obvious action was to do so, which would often help to spread the disease. There was no effective protection against plague until the introduction of a vaccine of dead plague bacilli by W. Haffkine in 1897,[28] only three years after the discovery of the organism, and no effective treatment until the development of the 'broad-spectrum' antibiotics in the 1950s. Earlier forms of treatment were numerous, varied and useless.

From the time of the Black Death in 1348–9 to the Great Plague of London in 1665 England was seldom, if ever, completely free from plague. The sixteenth century saw several serious outbreaks. Plague was then a well-known phenomenon, a considerable number of regulations to control the spread of the disease were issued, and numerous prescriptions for its treatment were published, many of which were still in use in the seventeenth century. Most were herbal mixtures, often including theriac (p. 39) or mithridatium (p. 40). Local treatment involved fomentation and incision of buboes; it was thought that free discharge of pus from these would rid the body of the poison.

In 1518, a year when nearly every town in England suffered from plague,[29] plague orders were issued in the king's name to the effect that the door of every infected house should be marked with a red cross and the inscription, 'Lord Have Mercy Upon Us.'[30] No occupant of an infected house was to walk abroad without carrying in his hand a rod four feet long and no clothing or bedding was to be sent out of the house for at least three months.[32] These orders were amended and added to in the many subsequent epidemics which occurred in English towns during and after the reign of Henry VIII. During severe epidemics nobody was allowed to leave the infected house.

In the seventeenth century there were three major epidemics of plague in London, in 1603, 1625 and 1665. Each spread to neighbouring towns and, in different degrees, throughout the country. In the intervening years London was seldom, if ever, entirely free from plague, and major epidemics occurred in other parts of England, but the London epidemics are the best documented and may be regarded as typical of plague in a city.

1603. The epidemic of 1603 started in March and reached a peak of 3385 plague deaths in a week in September.[33] Thomas Dekker, the playwright, described the state of the city at the height of the epidemic.

For he that durst (in the dead hours of gloomy midnight) have been so valiant as to have walkt through the still and melancholy streets, what thinke you should have bene his musicke? Surely the loude grones of raving sicke men, the strugling panges of soules departing: In every house griefe striking up an Allarum: Servants crying out for maisters: wives for husbands: parents for children, children for their mothers: here he should have met some frantickly running to knock up Sextons; there others fearfully sweating with Coffins, to steal forth dead bodies lest the fatall hand-writing of death should seale up their doores.[34]

This would be the cross and the inscription, 'Lord have mercy upon us'.

With a spell of cold weather in November the epidemic waned and by the first week of December, although the death rate was still high, refugees were returning to the city. By this time plague was raging throughout the country and London was safer than many other places. It is estimated that 22.6% of the population of London died of plague in 1603.[35]

1625. The next devastating epidemic of plague in England started in March 1625. By May the weekly death-rate from plague in London was 45 and by August it reached a peak of 4463.[36] The total recorded for the whole year for London and its out-parishes was 41,313; Slack estimates the mortality as 20.1% of the population.[37] The actual number of deaths from plague was probably higher because the death-rate reported from other causes was much higher than usual and probably included many plague deaths not diagnosed as such, either erroneously or to save the other occupants of the house from almost certain death if shut in. Many may have died from septicaemic or pneumonic plague, which would not be diagnosed as plague in the absence of buboes and other typical signs.

After August the epidemic began to decline in spite of the return of many refugees to the city and, from October, famine was a greater scourge than plague due to a bad harvest. Poor relief, though on a more generous scale than usual, was inadequate, and breakdown of civic discipline led to widespread looting. On 20 December an Order in Council proclaimed that the epidemic was over, although a few plague deaths were still being reported.[38] This epidemic did not involve as many towns as some of its predecessors but most places near London were affected and severe outbreaks of plague occurred in towns as widely separated as Exeter and Norwich.

1665. The last major epidemic of plague in England was the Great Plague of London in 1665. Shortly before Christmas 1664, two men died of plague in Drury Lane. The cause of death was certified by two physicians and a surgeon and published in the weekly Bill of Mortality.[39] No further cases were reported for six weeks though the total death rate rose considerably during this period and many of the deaths may have been due to plague. By the end of February the danger could no longer be concealed. The weekly plague mortality reached a peak of more than 7000 in June, after which it declined steadily until the end of the year. The official death toll from plague in London in 1665 came to 68,596,[40] but this is certainly an underestimate since most deaths of Quakers, Anabaptists and Jews were not recorded[41] and many deaths from plague must have been falsely attributed to other diseases to avoid compulsory segregation of the family in the infected house. Most authorities agree that the true figure would be about 100,000 out of a population of at least half a million, a mortality of nearly 20% of the inhabitants of London in one year. Although this was the highest gross mortality of any London plague it was lower as a percentage than in the epidemic of 1603, and probably that of 1625, because of the much larger population.

Pepys's *Diary* follows the development of the epidemic in the city.

24 May: In the Coffee-house, where all the news is of the Dutch being gone out and of the plague growing upon us in this town; and of remedies against it; some saying one thing and some another. *29 June*: By water to White Hall, where the court full of waggons and people ready to go out of town. This end of the town grows very bad of the plague. *25 July*: Sad the story of the plague in the City, it growing mightily. *16 August*: But, Lord! how sad a sight it is to see the streets empty of people and very few upon the 'Change! Jealous of every door that one sees shut up, lest it be the plague, and about us two shops in three, if not more, generally shut up.[42]

The clergyman, Thomas Vincent, gives an even more dramatic description of the state of London in August.

Now shops are shut in, people rare, and very few that walk about, insomuch that the grass begins to spring up in some places, and a deep silence almost in every place, especially within the walls; no rattling coaches, no prancing horses, no calling in customers, nor offering wares; no *London* cries sounding in the ears; if any voice be heard it is the groans of dying persons, breathing forth their last, and the funeral knells of them that are ready to be carried to their graves.[43]

Figure 20. Burying the dead during the Great Plague of London. From a contemporary print (courtesy of the London Library).

John Evelyn wrote in his diary on 7 September:

> Came home, there perishing now neare ten-thousand poore Creatures
> weekely; however I went all along the City and suburbs from *Kent-
> Streete* to *St James's*, a dismal passage and dangerous, to see so many
> Coffines exposed in the streetes and the streetes thin of people, the
> shops shut up, and all in mournful silence, as not knowing whose
> turn might be next.[44]

The dead were collected in carts, which patrolled the streets, and were
buried, as in previous epidemics, after sunset, until the number of burials
made this impracticable. Only at the height of the epidemic were dead
bodies seen in the streets or burials undertaken by day. The activity in a
graveyard is depicted in a contemporary print (Fig. 20). Nurses were
appointed to tend those sick of the plague but these were women of the
poorest class, often servants abandoned by their masters, who had fled the
city. They were frequently suspected of smothering their patients in order
to steal their possessions.[45]

By September the mortality had begun to fall. There were as many
cases of plague but fewer deaths. As soon as the Bills of Mortality showed
fewer deaths the population herded together without precautions and many
returned to London and there contracted plague. With the onset of severe
frost in November the epidemic diminished rapidly and, by December,
the weekly death rate was less than 300.[46] A few cases of plague still
occurred in London in 1666 and 1667, since when there has been no
major epidemic.

During 1665 every town and village near London suffered from plague.
Severe outbreaks occurred also in Yarmouth, Colchester, Southampton
and Peterborough and more limited ones in many other towns. Centres
of plague in 1666 included Colchester, Winchester, Deptford, Greenwich,
Deal and Portsmouth.[47] For towns outside London few details are available
except, in some cases, the number of deaths. In Colchester these amounted
to more than one-third of the population, the highest mortality in any
provincial town since the Black Death in 1348–9.[48] An epidemic was
reported in Nottingham in 1667, since when England has been free from
plague except for scattered outbreaks, usually in sea-ports, as late as the
twentieth century.

Smallpox

Although Rhazes (p. 41) had described, in his Treatise on *Smallpox and Measles* (*c.* AD 910), the difference between these diseases, they were still confused in the seventeenth century, when Thomas Phaire (p. 49) regarded them as different manifestations of the same disease.[49] As late as 1660 the Duke of Gloucester, brother of King Charles II, was reported 'to have a disease between the smallpox and the measles',[50] of which he died, but most seventeenth-century physicians regarded smallpox and measles as entirely different diseases, although the treatment might be the same for both. There was some confusion also between the great pox (syphilis) and smallpox (variola) though the clinical features are quite different.

Smallpox is an acute fever, caused by infection with the *Variola* virus, a minute organism which is transmitted by droplet infection in the breath or by contamination from the skin. Gideon Harvey (p. 9) believed (correctly) that it is usually conveyed by particles in the air.[51] There is a characteristic spotty rash and the spots become vesicles, which become pustules, which dry up and the scabs separate, leaving pitted scars (pocks). One attack of smallpox usually confers immunity for life.

Thomas Sydenham distinguished 'distinct pox', a mild disease with isolated pustules, from the severe and often fatal 'flux-pox', where the pustules are numerous and run together.[52] In some severe and fatal cases bleeding occurs into the skin, lungs, kidneys and alimentary canal (haemorrhagic smallpox). Until the introduction of inoculation with smallpox by Lady Wortley Montagu about 1720, the safer vaccination with cowpox (*Vaccinia*) invented by Edward Jenner in 1798, and the modern vaccination with glycerinated calf lymph since 1881[53] there was no effective preventive against smallpox and there is still no specific treatment.

Although smallpox was common in England in the sixteenth century it was not regarded as a serious malady and did not reach epidemic proportions until the end of the century, when it became more prevalent and more lethal. Two modern writers conclude that the virus must have undergone mutation or that a new and more virulent strain may have been introduced from Africa or the Orient.[54] Most people in the seventeenth century had an attack of smallpox and many died.

The first report of an epidemic of smallpox in seventeenth-century London was by the Venetian Ambassador in October 1605. 'There has been some question of proroguing Parliament, on account of a renewal of the plague during these last two weeks, but that has now been recognised not as plague, but as small-pox, which is very common here.'[55] Other serious epidemics occurred in 1609, 1621 and 1623.[56] In the first annual Bills of Mortality to record individual causes of death other than plague (1629) 72 deaths were attributed to 'flox, small-pox and measles', 'flox' being Sydenham's 'flux-pox' (p. 158); in 1634 the figure was 1654. By 1641 smallpox was distinguished from measles and from then until the Restoration in 1660 there were epidemics of smallpox every few years, with weekly deaths sometimes exceeding 100.[57] During the remainder of the century there was no year when no smallpox deaths were recorded in London; the lowest number (38) was in 1666 (the year after the Great Plague) and the highest (2981) in 1681.[58] The epidemic in 1681 followed two hot, dry summers and was accompanied by an epidemic of infantile diarrhoea (p. 166). Epidemics of smallpox were reported from Cambridge in 1674, Bath in 1675, Norwich in 1681 and Leeds in 1699, but the number of deaths was recorded only for London.[59]

Contemporary medical opinion was that smallpox was less severe in children than in adults. According to Walter Harris, whose work was greatly admired by Sydenham: 'The *Small-pox* and *Measles* of infants, which commonly are no more than a mild and quiet Effervescence of their Blood, seldom are attended with any danger.'[60] The disease did not spare the aristocracy, many of whom died of it, including Queen Mary in 1694.[61] Sydenham attributed many of the deaths to failure to use his cooling regime (p. 65) or to draw off enough blood, whereas Gideon Harvey contended that blood-letting in smallpox was more likely to kill than cure.[62] He thought it best to leave smallpox untreated but symptoms might be relieved by one of the following mixtures. For a child: 'Take of Chamomile Flowers and Elder Flowers, of each half a handful, boil them in Posset, made with Smallbeer very little hopt, to a pint and strain it.'[63] For an adult he recommended a potion of 'Figs, Currants, Tragacanth, Fennel and Columbine seeds, and Saffron boiled in Barley Water.'[64] Most of those who recovered from smallpox had disfiguring pockmarks on the face, though some physicians claimed that this could be prevented by opening the pustules with a golden needle.[65] Various ointments were prescribed but were ineffective.

Although vaccination was available from 1798 there was considerable opposition to it from doctors and from the lay public. Smallpox was still a scourge in England until the end of the nineteenth century and small outbreaks occurred in the first half of the twentieth. An outstanding success of modern medicine is the virtual abolition of smallpox by widespread vaccination.

Measles

Linked with smallpox by Rhazes and other Arab writers, and regarded in the Middle Ages and Tudor times as a mild form of smallpox, measles was listed as a separate disease in the London Bills of Mortality from 1641. Measles is caused by a different virus from that which causes smallpox and the fever is accompanied at first by signs of upper respiratory infection and later by a blotchy rash, which does not form pustules or leave scars. The disease, which is highly infectious, is spread by droplet infection from the patient's breath and one attack usually confers lifelong immunity. Gideon Harvey observed that it is usually less dangerous than smallpox but can be fatal.[66] Since recovery is usual the incidence of the disease cannot be estimated from the Bills of Mortality but the recorded deaths from measles reveal epidemics in London in 1656, 1664, 1670 and 1674;[67] in the last and most severe of these epidemics 795 deaths were attributed to measles and the unusually high death rates from 'convulsions' and 'teeth' suggest that some of these were infantile deaths related to the measles epidemic.[68]

The country doctor, John Symcotts (p. 29), described the 'red fever' (probably measles).

> Many children fell very sick in their heads and stomach, desiring nothing but cold beer, and some, milk. They fell presently into a general redness of skin all over, were very feverish with high and yellow waters, all of which were much molested with sore throats for a time.[69]

Sydenham's description of an attack of measles is so precise that it could not be confused with any other disease.

> It chiefly invades Infants and all those that were together in the same House. It began with Shaking and Shivering . . . the second Day it ended in a perfect *Fever*, with violent Sickness, Thirst, and want of Appetite; the Tongue was white but not dry; there was a small Cough, with a heaviness of the Head and Eyes, accompany'd with a continual Drowsiness . . . the patient sneezes, as if he had taken cold . . . he

vomits, but is oftener troubled with a Looseness, and the Stools are greenish . . . The Symptoms increase for the most part till the fourth Day, and then generally . . . little red Spots, like Flea-bites, begin to come out about the Forehead and other parts of the Face, and being increased in Number and Bigness branch into one another and . . . are elevated a little above the Skin; and their Protuberances may be perceived by a gentle touch, tho they can scarce be seen; these Spots spread themselves by degrees from the Face, which first they only possessed, to the Breast, Belly, Thighs and Legs; but they affect the Trunk and Members with redness only, without any sensible Inequality of the Skin . . . On the sixth Day, or thereabouts, the Skin breaking and the Pustles [*sic*] drying off, the Forehead and Face grow rough and at the same time the Spots in the other Parts of the Body are very large and very red. About the eighth Day the Spots in the Face vanish, and are scarce perceived in the rest of the Body; but on the ninth Day they quite disappear. The Face and Members and sometimes the whole Body seems as it were to be sprinkled with Bran.[70]

Sydenham noted that fever and respiratory complications often became severe as the rash faded.

Andrew Boorde, in the sixteenth century, had kept his measles patients warm, on a light diet, and administered theriac or mithridatium.[71] This 'warm' treatment was still prevalent in the seventeenth century and was adopted by Symcotts, whose treatment was 'keeping them in bed, or very warm; inward and outward medicines for the throat and cough; and, when the heat went off a little, gently purging them'[72] but Sydenham thought it was dangerous and treated measles as he treated smallpox by keeping the patient out of bed as long as possible and avoiding artificial heating (p. 65). He also prescribed a cough mixture:

Take of the Oil of sweet Almonds, two Ounces; of Syrup of Violets and Maidenhair, each one Ounce; of white Sugar-candy a sufficient quantity: mingle them, and make a linctus [a syrupy medicine], whereof let him lick often, especially when his Cough troubles him.[73]

There were severe epidemics of measles in England with high mortality in the eighteenth and nineteenth centuries. A marked decline in mortality in the twentieth century may be attributed to improved living conditions and more effective treatment of complications, such as pneumonia and encephalitis, which are commoner in undernourished children and may still be fatal. A protective vaccine against measles is now administered at the age of 9 months, prior to which the infant has some protection from antibodies in the mother's blood.

Typhus

Another epidemic disease, typhus, is caused by a micro-organism *Rickettsia prowazeki*, larger than the virus of smallpox but smaller than the bacillus of plague. The incidence of the disease in the seventeenth century is difficult to assess because it was often confused with other fevers, especially the enteric group (p. 164). John Huxham, in 1755, was the first to make a clear distinction between malignant fever (typhus) and slow nervous fever (typhoid).[74] Until 1829, deaths from typhus and from enteric fevers were not distinguished in the Bills of Mortality.[75]

Typhus, also called 'gaol fever', 'famine fever', and 'spotted fever', is an acute fever, often with delirium or stupor, a spotty rash and sometimes diarrhoea. The infection is louse-borne; hence its prevalence in the gaols, where louse infestation was high. Typhus epidemics were also associated with famine, which lowered resistance to infection, but spotted fever was an unfortunate term because many infectious diseases have a spotty rash and that of typhus is not typical.

In the Tudor period there had been at least three severe outbreaks of gaol fever, originating in the law-courts at Cambridge in 1522, Oxford in 1577 and Exeter in 1586.[76] At these 'Black Assizes' many who were present contracted typhus and died. The louse is no respecter of persons and must have been responsible for spreading the disease to judges, lawyers, jurymen and members of the public attending the trials; its significance was not recognised and the epidemic was attributed to the contaminated air of the gaol being carried into the court by the prisoners.

During the First Civil War typhus was prevalent in Oxfordshire and Berkshire.[77] When Sir Thomas Fairfax defeated the Royalist garrison of Reading and entered the town in 1643 he found it heavily infected with typhus and lost so many men in the ensuing epidemic that he could not proceed to attack Oxford, which might have brought the war to an early close.[78] The small Devonshire town of Tiverton, occupied by both armies in the course of 1644, suffered very severely from typhus.[79]

Typhus was endemic in London in the seventeenth century, with epidemics in 1623–4 , 1685–6 and 1694,[80] and a severe outbreak in Bristol in 1698 followed a succession of bad harvests.[81] It is odd that, when

Sydenham described the typical clinical picture of typhus in the 1685 epidemic, he called it a 'new fever'. In a rather long-winded description of the symptoms he mentions cough, headache, delirium, a spotty rash and continual fever, often worst at night.[82] The best description of the condition is by Thomas Willis:

> The beginnings of the sickness were scarce perceived: for arising without immoderate heat, or more sharp thirst, it induced in the whole body a great debility . . . The stomack was ready to loath any victuals, and to be grieved at anything put into it, and yet not easie to vomit. The sick were unfit for any motion, and only lov'd to be idle or to lie down upon the Bed . . . they complained of a heavy *vertigo*, a tingling of the ears, and often a great tumult and perturbation of the brain . . . In many Children, and not seldom in Women . . . Speech failed them and so the sick have lain . . . sometimes for the space of a whole month, without taking any notice of the by-standers and with an involuntary flux of their excrements . . . In almost all the belly was for the most part loose, casting forth plentifully, now yellow, now thin and serous excrement, with a great stink . . . The urine . . . was highly red.[83]

Wasting was extreme in all the patients, some had severe catarrh, and some had a rash of small red spots, smaller than the 'tokens', which were a feature of plague (p. 152). Most children recovered from the disease.

Sydenham treated typhus, like most other fevers, by bleeding and purging and he refused to let the patient be overheated. He sometimes ordered the head to be shaved in order to cool it and so prevent the onset of delirium. Of the various remedies he prescribed one of the simplest was: 'Take of Fountain-water, one Pint; of Rose-water, of the Juice of Lemons, of white Sugar, each four Ounces; boil them over a gentle Fire till all the Scum be risen: Take three ounces at pleasure.'[84] Willis also bled and purged and he attempted to promote sweating by administering powdered pearls of spirit of hartshorn.[85]

Further epidemics of typhus occurred in the eighteenth and nineteenth centuries, particularly in the insanitary slums of the new industrial towns, but in the twentieth century it has been limited in England to small localised outbreakes in sea-ports. A protective vaccine is now available and the causative organism is susceptible to broad-spectrum antibiotics.

Enteric fevers

The enteric fevers (typhoid and paratyphoid) were confused with typhus until the nineteenth century (p. 162), although the clinical features and mode of spread are different. The organisms responsible are bacteria (*Salmonella typhi* and *S. paratyphi*), the infection is primarily of the alimentary canal, and the disease is usually transmitted in contaminated drinking water. The rash, which may occur, may be confused with that of typhus, and bronchitis and delirium may occur in both diseases. Hence, although the enteric fevers were almost certainly present in seventeenth-century England, it is impossible to assess their prevalence.

Thomas Willis, in his *Practice of Physick* (1684), described a 'putrid feaver', which was probably typhoid.

> The first assault is for the most part accompanied with a shivering or horror . . . heat and sometimes sweat follow upon the shivering . . . afterwards a certain remission of the heat follows . . . A pain arises in the Head or Loins . . . also a nauseousness or a vomiting offends the stomach.

As the disease progresses 'the sick complain of intolerable thirst, besides a pain of the head, pertinacious wakings, and oftentimes a delirium.'[86] Diarrhoea is usual, sometimes starting at the beginning of the disease, sometimes later on, when it is a favourable sign. Sydenham believed that the 'putrid fever' often followed smallpox; he prescribed bleeding and paregoric (a preparation of opium with a constipating action)[87] but found that the sufferer from both diseases was unlikely to recover.

The enteric fevers are still common today in countries where sanitation is as primitive as it was in seventeenth-century England, though rare in modern Europe, but 'food poisoning', due to contamination with *S. paratyphi* or related organisms and characterised by acute diarrhoea and vomiting, can occur wherever preparation of food is undertaken without due attention to hygiene. Protective inoculation against the enteric fevers is available but the protection is short-lived and inoculation must be repeated after six months if there is repeated exposure to infection. Although the organisms are susceptible to broad-spectrum antibiotics typhoid is still a dangerous disease.

Dysentery

Dysentery ('the bloody flux') is mentioned in Graunt's *Natural and Politicall Observations on the Bills of Mortality* (1662) as a serious epidemic disease in London and is described in contemporary textbooks of medicine. 'The *Dysentery* is a bloody and sometimes a purulent Flux of the Belly, with a gnawing of the tunicles [coverings] of the guts.'[88] The commonest dysentery in England is (and probably was) due to infection with bacteria of the genus, *Shigella*. It is spread by contamination of water, food, or hands with infected faeces and may be spread by flies; it is therefore commonest where sanitation is poor, and in summer. A mild infection may not be noticed but a severe one causes copious diarrhoea with blood and mucus in the stools and may be fatal. Such deaths might be recorded as 'flux' or 'griping in the guts'.

According to Sydenham:

Sometimes it begins with a Shaking and Shivering and a Heat of the whole Body follows as is usual in *Fevers*, and soon after the *Gripes* [colic] and Stools; but oftentimes there is no appearance of a *Fever* going before, for the *Gripes* begin and stools soon follow. These mucous stools are streaked with Blood, but sometimes there is no blood at all mixed with them through the whole course of the Disease; yet notwithstanding, if the Stools are frequent with *Gripes*, and a mucous Filth, the disease may as properly be call'd a *Dysentery*, as if Blood flow'd out with them.[89]

Bruel observed that

the fayling of the stomack, increase of thirst, continuall flux of the belly, are bad signs; also if the urine bee not answerable to that which is drunke, and if black excrements be voyded, the body being leane, if parcels of fat and flesh and pieces of the guts be voyded as also if the patient be weake, the flux is mortal.[90]

There was no protection against dysentery in the seventeenth century, since its cause was unknown, but numerous medicines were prescribed for its treatment. The most effective, prescribed by Sydenham and several other physicians for the relief of diarrhoea, was laudanum (tincture of opium), usually mixed with other herbal remedies. A domestic remedy, which might give some relief, was prescribed by the Countess of Kent (p. 133), who also prescribed a soothing enema: 'Take white starch made of Wheat two or three spoonfuls and also new Milk from the Cow, stir these together and give it to the party grieved in manner of a glister.'[91]

Dysentery still occurs where sanitation is primitive and is a common disease of armies in the field. It is less dangerous today because the organisms are sensitive to some antibiotic drugs and replacement of the fluid loss, not regarded as important in the seventeenth century, is now appreciated as an essential part of treatment.

Summer diarrhoea

Summer diarrhoea of infants was usually recorded in seventeenth-century Bills of Mortality as 'griping in the guts' or as 'convulsions', which were common accompaniments of the diarrhoea. The disease is due to infection by any of a variety of micro-organisms, especially today the bacterium, *Escherichia coli*. It is commonly conveyed from excreta to food by flies (hence the prevalence of the disease in summer) or by human carriers handling food. As might be expected, epidemics of infantile diarrhoea were particularly severe during hot, dry summers, as in 1669, 1681 and 1684; mortality was particularly high in 1684.[92]

Walter Harris, in his *Treatise of the Acute Diseases of Children* (1689), recommended for gripes and fever in an infant a powder of crabs' claws,[93] alternatively chalk, coral or pearls might be administered, with rhubarb later (which would make the diarrhoea worse) or small doses of laudanum (which would ease it).[94] Pechey favoured a compound powder of crabs' claws and pearls but attempted to relieve gripes with a soothing enema or by applying heat to the abdomen.[95] Robert Pemell commented that diarrhoea with 'gripings in the belly' might be due to worms in the intestine, in which case these must be eliminated (p. 67).

The death rate from summer diarrhoea is still high among undernourished children in primitive communities. Death is usually due to dehydration, which would not be understood in the seventeenth century; the fluid lost in the stools would not be replaced nor would drugs effective against the causative organisms be available. Fluid replacement is now the basis of treatment and broad-spectrum antibiotics are of value except when the causative organism is a virus.

Influenza

The term, 'influenza', was first introduced into English in 1743 by John

Huxham, a physician in Plymouth[96], but there is little doubt that some of the epidemics of fever with respiratory infection as early as the sixteenth century were manifestations of this disease. Few epidemics of fever in the first half of the seventeenth century had the typical characteristics of influenza but epidemics, probably of influenza, occurred in England in 1658, 1675, 1679, 1688 and 1693.[97]

Although the disease could not be positively identified before the discovery of the influenza virus in 1933,[98] the description by Thomas Willis of the epidemic in 1658 leaves little doubt that it was due to influenza.

> About the end of April, suddenly a Distemper arose, as if sent by some blast of the stars, which laid hold on very many together: that in some towns, in the space of a week, above a thousand people fell sick together. The particular symptom of this disease, and which first invaded the sick, was a troublesome cough, with great spitting, also a catarrh fallin [sic] down on the palat [sic], throat and nostrils: also it was accompanied with a feaverish distemper, joyned with heat and thirst, want of appetite, a spontaneous weariness, and a grievous pain in the back and limbs.[99]

Sydenham described the 1675 epidemic as 'Epidemic Coughs with a Pleurisy and Peripneumonia coming upon them'[100] but his description is confused by an attempt to fit it into his theory of epidemic constitutions. He observed that the epidemic was widespread but brief.

Both Willis and Sydenham believed in light diet, blood-letting, and relief of the cough. Sydenham's cough lozenges had the following composition:

> Take of Sugar-candy two Pounds and a half, boil it in a sufficient quantity of common Water till it sticks to the Fingers; and then add of the Pouder of Liquorice, Elecampane, the Seeds of Anise and Angelica, of each half an Ounce; of the Pouders of Orris, and of Flowers of Sulphur, each two Drams; of the Chymical Oil of the Seeds of Anise two Scruples: Make Tablets according to Art, which let him always carry in his pocket and take one of them often.'[101]

There was no specific treatment for influenza in the seventeenth century and there is none today, though various drugs have been and are used to relieve the symptoms. Epidemics still occur and the pandemic in 1918 and 1919, which was accompanied by bacterial respiratory infection, was the most widespread and one of the most lethal diseases in history; it was responsible for more deaths throughout the world than the First World War. In England and Wales there were about 150,000 deaths from influenza in 1918 and 1919.[102] As for many other virus diseases, a protective vaccine is now available, but it is less effective than the others, presumably because it gives protection only against a particular strain or strains of the virus and there are many strains.

Other epidemic diseases

Scarlet fever (scarlatina) is a fever with sore throat and a fairly uniform red rash over the body, with some flaking or peeling of the skin when the rash fades; it is a reaction, by those who suffer it, to throat infection with a bacterium, *Streptococcus haemolyticus*. Sydenham regarded it as a mild disease (p. oo) and Dr Richard Morton thought it was merely a form of measles in which the rash is continuous.[103] If diphtheria, a throat infection with *Corynebacterium diphtheriae*, occurred in seventeenth-century England it was not recognised as such and may have been diagnosed as scarlet fever in spite of the absence of the typical rash. Scarlet fever has varied in severity; no epidemics were recorded in the seventeenth century, severe and lethal epidemics occurred in the eighteenth and nineteenth; today it is rare and cured by antibiotics.

Whooping cough (chincough, pertussis) is a respiratory infection with a bacterium (*Bordetella pertussis*), characterised in young children by a crowing inspiration (the 'whoop') after a bout of coughing. The disease has been known since medieval times[104] and is described by Walter Harris in his *Acute Diseases of Infants* (p. 66). Sydenham regarded it as a complication of some other acute infection and treated it with bleeding and purging.[105] It is seldom fatal and few cases would be treated by a physician; it is not mentioned in the Bills of Mortality until 1701.[106] Hence it is impossible to ascertain whether epidemics of whooping cough occurred in the seventeenth century. A protective vaccine is now available and the causative organism is sensitive to some antibiotics, but once the 'whooping' stage is reached only a cough suppressant is of value.

Chickenpox (varicella) is a viral infection, usually of children, characterised by a vesicular rash, not unlike that of smallpox in appearance but differing in distribution and the vesicles do not become pustules. It is very infectious but seldom dangerous and appeared only occasionally, as 'swine pox', in the Bills of Mortality.[107] Since it was commonest in the poor, who did not consult physicians, and seldom fatal, it is impossible to tell whether epidemics of chickenpox occurred in the seventeenth century. Epidemics occur today and there is no specific treatment but most cases are mild and uncomplicated.

Mumps (epidemic parotitis) is a virus infection, causing tender swelling of one or both parotid (salivary) glands in the cheeks. If it occurs at puberty or shortly after it may be complicated by inflammation of testes or ovaries. Mumps was described by Hippocrates but disregarded until the sixteenth century.[108] Although individual cases are recorded in the seventeenth century there is no record of any epidemic, probably because spontaneous recovery is usual. Although not so infectious as some other viral diseases (measles and chickenpox) epidemics of mumps occur today, but no specific treatment is available and most cases are uncomplicated.

CHAPTER 11

The Legacy of the Seventeenth Century

There were far more literate and educated Englishmen in the eighteenth than in the seventeenth century and their attitudes to religion, magic and science were, on the whole, vastly different. The national Church had been forced by public opinion to become more tolerant and non-conformists were no longer persecuted, though they were still excluded from the two English universities and from positions of public responsibility. Belief in the supernatural had waned, though it never disappeared, and natural explanations were sought for natural events. Whereas at the beginning of the seventeenth century the opinion of ancient authors had been widely regarded as the ultimate authority, by the end of the century these views were challenged and rejected if they failed to agree with observation and reason. The scope of observation was greatly extended by improvements in the microscope, which made possible further developments in embryology and pathology.

The attitude to science proposed by Francis Bacon early in the seventeenth century, adopted by the Royal Society, and reinforced by leading English scientists, proved a strong base for further scientific advances which occurred in the eighteenth century. Bacon believed that the purpose of science is to understand and control nature for the benefit of mankind and, though the scientific interests of the members of the Royal Society were diverse, their aims were mostly utilitarian and remained so in the eighteenth century. Major scientific discoveries, such as the law of gravity and the circulation of the blood, had increased man's knowledge of nature but an even more important legacy from the seventeenth century was acceptance of the scientific method of testing hypotheses by observation and experiment.

Medical science

The eighteenth century started with an understanding of the circulation of the blood, which made nonsense of traditional ideas that blood-letting should be from particular sites in particular diseases. There was also some knowledge of the mechanism of respiration and of the transport of some gas, as yet unidentified, from air to blood in the lungs. Boyle's *Sceptical Chymist* (1661), according to Singer, 'opens the modern period of chemistry and marks the end of the doctrine of the four elements of the Artistotelians'.[1] Some chemical reactions were known to occur in the body, for instance digestion of food by gastric and pancreatic juices, but the vast field of biochemistry which explains living processes in terms of chemical reactions, was still to be explored.

The understanding of illness had made some advance in the seventeenth century with recognition of individual diseases taking the place of the concept of disturbed balance of the classical 'humours'. Rejection of the humoral theory was an important contribution to the progress of medical science. Hermann Boerhaave, who graduated in medicine at Leyden in 1693 and whose teaching dominated the first half of the eighteenth century, fused traditional and new medicine into a 'well-organised complete system'.[2] He had a laboratory for chemical and physiological experiments as well as hospital beds for clinical teaching and taught his students a scientific approach to the diagnosis and treatment of disease. Like Sydenham he studied the effects of drugs on his patients and was aware of the dangers of excessive treatment.

Some physicians, including Sydenham, had tried to classify diseases as biologists were classifying plants and animals. Although this did not explain the diseases it paved the way for Giovanni Battista Morgagni, in the eighteenth century to establish pathology as a science with his book, *De sedibus et causis morborum* (1761). Morgagni compared clinical with post-mortem findings to relate diseases to the organ or organs principally affected, but he was unaware of the nature of infection although about 80% of deaths in the eighteenth century were due to infectious diseases.[3] It was not until the identification of disease-producing bacteria by Robert Koch in 1875[4] and of viruses by Friedrich Löffler in 1898[5] that infectious diseases could be understood. There was, as yet, no concept of disease due to dietary deficiency (except scurvy), to disorders of the endocrine glands, or to inherent defects of metabolism (the body's capacity to transform food materials into its own substance, energy and waste products).

Perhaps the most important contribution of seventeenth-century medical science to subsequent centuries was vital statistics. The analysis of Bills of Mortality by John Graunt and William Petty (p. 89) provided an objective index of the state of health of the community, not just the individual, and of the prevalence of particular diseases. Sir John Pringle's *Observations on Diseases in the Army* (1745) was a logical sequel to the earlier works; he became Physician to the King and President of the Royal Society.[6] Analysis of biological data, refined and extended in later years by the development of statistical methods, is the basis of medical investigation today.

Medical practice

Medical diagnosis improved considerably during the seventeenth century and, by the beginning of the eighteenth, was usually based on a careful case history and examination, without such discredited procedures as uroscopy and astrology. Most medical practitioners in London were apothecaries; at the beginning of the eighteenth century it has been estimated that London had about 1000 apothecaries and sixty to eighty physicians.[7] By this time the country or small town practitioner was usually called 'surgeon-apothecary' whatever his training.[8]

Medical treatment by physician or apothecary was little changed since the Middle Ages, though prescriptions were generally simpler. Blood-letting usually by a surgeon, and purgation were still the basis of treatment of most illnesses and most prescriptions were of ineffective herbs, but one very useful plant drug, the bark of the *Cinchona* tree, known at the time as Peruvian bark (p. 62), was established as effective in the treatment of ague (malaria) though its active principle (quinine) was not isolated until 1820.[9] Another useful drug, first imported from South America in the seventeenth century, was ipecac, the dried root of *Cephaelis ipecacuanha*, used as an emetic and, in smaller doses, in the treatment of dysentery. Its active principle (emetine), isolated in 1829,[10] is still used in the treatment of one type of dysentery, amoebic dysentery due to infection with *Entamoeba histolitica*. The prevention and treatment of scurvy with fruit juice was recommended as early as 1617 by John Woodall (p. 109) but was not generally adopted until more than a century later.

Some chemical remedies, such as antimony as an emetic and mercury for the treatment of syphilis, were effective though dangerous, and gold was prescribed on the principle that it was the most precious metal, though it is unlikely to have had any therapeutic action. Some of the more repulsive remedies of the seventeenth century were abandoned in the eighteenth but some traditional medicines, such as coral or the horn of the mythical unicorn (p. 47) were still prescribed. Robert Boyle, though not a doctor, showed considerable insight into diseases such as nephritis, kidney stone, and heart failure in his book, *Of the Reconcileableness of Specifick Medicines to the Corpuscular Philosophy* (1685), in which he recommended the use of specific medicines for particular diseases, a practice which became more prevalent in the eighteenth century. The seventeenth century also saw the end of the unprofitable dispute between galenists and paracelsians; by the end of the century most doctors were prescribing herbal or inorganic preparations, whichever seemed most appropriate.

The apothecary

After the Rose decision in 1703 (p. 6) apothecaries could legitimately prescribe as well as dispense medicine, but they were to charge only for the medicine and not for the advice. Nevertheless, they derived a very adequate income from their charge for the remedies they recommended. In effect the apothecary became the general practitioner of the eighteenth century, though the term dates only from the nineteenth. Training was normally by apprenticeship, as in the past, but it was possible for the son of a liveryman to be admitted to the Society of Apothecaries without the experience if he passed the examination and paid a higher fee.[11] By the Apothecaries' Act of 1815 the Society's diploma entitled the holder to practise medicine and surgery anywhere in England and Wales.[12] The Licence of the Society of Apothecaries (L. S. A.), since 1907 the Licence in Medicine and Surgery of the Society of Apothecaries (L. M. S. S. A.) is a registrable qualification to practise medicine and surgery in Britain. Since 1827 the training and examination have included midwifery.

Surgery

The barber-surgeons at the beginning of the eighteenth century had often learnt their trade on the battlefield and had more experience of treating wounds than of other surgical operations. They applied oils, ointments and plasters to wounds, as in the past, and virtually all wounds were infected.

The leading surgeons of the period were French or German. Most English surgeons had little education and no training other than apprenticeship. An exception was William Cheselden, a surgeon at St Thomas's Hospital and, later, at the newly founded St George's Hospital. He was well educated and an accomplished anatomist and artist, noted particularly for the speed and skill with which he operated for stone in the bladder, speed being very important in the days before anaesthesia.[13] Later in the century Percivall Pott at St Bartholomew's Hospital devised many new and successful operations[14] and John Hunter, a student of Cheselden and Pott, was one of the first surgeons to base his treatment on scientific studies of anatomy and physiology. According to Garrison, Hunter found surgery a mechanical art and left it an experimental science.[15] The modern epoch in surgery dates only from the nineteenth century, with the introduction of effective anaesthesia to abolish the severe pain previously associated with surgical operations and, later in the century, with the practice of antiseptic and eventually aseptic operating techniques to combat infection.

Midwifery

Childbirth, at the beginning of the eighteenth century, was still very dangerous for mother and child, especially if conducted by an unskilled midwife. The expert man-midwife was becoming more fashionable for those who could afford his fees. William Smellie, a Scotsman, learnt his midwifery in Paris and set up a school of midwifery in London in 1739, where, as Willughby had done (p. 122), he stressed the importance of non-interference in normal labour; he also devised an improved version of the Chamberlens' obstetric forceps.[16] His pupil, William Hunter, John Hunter's elder brother, became the leading man-midwife of his period, though he seldom used forceps.[17]

The modern epoch in midwifery, as in surgery, dates from the introduction of anaesthesia and asepsis. No successful Caesarian section was performed in England with survival of mother and child until 1793[18] but this is now the treatment of choice when labour is obstructed by malpresentation of the child or a narrow or deformed birth canal.

Empirics and quacks

Unqualified practitioners of medicine flourished in the eighteenth as in the seventeenth century and their treatment might or might not be orthodox. The reformer, John Wesley's *Primitive Physick* (1747), recommended simple medicines and single drugs[19] and the Irish clergyman and philosopher, George Berkeley, prescribed tar-water for many ailments.[20] William Read, a competent but unqualified eye surgeon, was appointed oculist to Queen Anne[21] and a quack, Joshua Ward, treated King George II.[22]

There are still quack doctors in England, though not in such large numbers as in the seventeenth century. The mountebank (p. 141) is no longer with us and the term, 'quack', is applied today to anyone who practises medicine without the conventional training and examinations required by the General Medical Council (established in 1858) and due inclusion of his name in the Medical Register. There is no law against quacks, provided they do not pretend to be 'registered medical practitioners' and a registered practitioner is not required to practise orthodox medicine but must not associate professionally with an unregistered practitioner. Secret remedies, such as were sold even by reputable physicians in the seventeenth century, are no longer permitted; some of the traditional drugs are still popular but the constituents of a medicine must be printed on the label.

Medical organisation

The eighteenth century inherited the College of Physicians of London, the Worshipful Society of Apothecaries, and the Company of Barber-Surgeons. Most professional training was still by apprenticeship; this was organised by the apothecaries and by the surgeons but the College of Physicians offered little teaching and was mainly concerned with tests for qualification.[23] From the early eighteenth century the College grew in numbers and in influence. In 1851 it became the Royal College of Physicians[24] and, since the Medical Act of 1858, its Licentiate has been an official qualification for general practice and its Membership a qualification as a physician. The Fellowship remains the senior qualification as a physician.

From 1703 the apothecaries had the legal right to treat patients as well as to dispense medicines, a right conferred on them by the Apothecaries'

Act of 1815[25] and still valid. Surgeons were still regarded as inferior to physicians, even after 1745 when they were formally separated from the barbers,[26] and did not receive equal status until the creation of the Royal College of Surgeons of England in 1800.[27] By the end of the seventeenth century, however, their training was improving as many potential surgeons chose apprenticeship at a hospital instead of that provided by the Company of Barber-Surgeons. In the seventeenth century both St Bartholomew's and St Thomas's admitted such students, though neither offered courses of lectures until the eighteenth century. Surgery was not yet taught at universities.

No new general hospitals were established in London in the seventeenth century; St Bartholomew's and St Thomas's were both earlier foundations. In the eighteenth-century hospitals proliferated not only in London but throughout the country. In London Guy's, St George's, London, and Middlesex Hospitals were all established by 1745.[28] By the end of the century nearly every county and many of the larger towns had hospitals, some with teaching facilities, and these were supplemented by charitable dispensaries, also used for teaching. The new hospitals and dispensaries were not supported by the state but by the local authorities.

The universities of Oxford and Cambridge still offered medical instruction based on classical texts and their degrees of Bachelor and Doctor of Medicine were accepted by the College of Physicians as qualification to practise. In the eighteenth century some clinical experience was demanded as well; this could be gained in England but was better at Padua, Montpellier, Leyden or some other medical school which offered practical teaching. The Edinburgh medical school, whose foundation dates from 1685, though it was not fully formed before 1726,[29] was based on the Leyden pattern and attracted many English students. It had some brilliant teachers and by the end of the eighteenth century was the leading medical school in Britain.

Formal qualification to practise medicine was still widely ignored and, when a certificate of competence was obtained, it was more often issued by authority of the Church than by the official professional bodies. Not until 1858 did this become the prerogative of the newly constituted General Medical Council.

Public health

The only major contribution of the seventeenth century to public health was the identification of some major diseases and the recording of their incidence in the Bills of Mortality. Little was done, apart from attempts to segregate plague patients and contacts, to limit the spread of infectious disease; and sanitation in the cities was still inferior to that in ancient Rome. Efficient sewerage and clean drinking water were not provided until lack of them was found to be responsible for the rapid spread of cholera in the epidemics of this disease which caused havoc in English towns in 1832 and some subsequent years.[30]

The major change in the pattern of life in eighteenth-century England was the urbanisation which accompanied the Industrial Revolution and forced labourers into crowded and insanitary dwellings. Furthermore, working conditions in the factories were such as to add to the toll of illness and accidents. The public conscience was not roused until the publication in 1842 of Edwin Chadwick's report on *The Sanitary Conditions of the Labouring Classes* and the first major attempt to improve these living conditions was the great Public Health Act of 1875.[31] It follows that the eighteenth century inherited from the seventeenth and transmitted to the nineteenth living conditions which predisposed much of the population to illness. In the nineteenth century the health of the whole community became for the first time a major responsibility of the medical profession and of the state. Although the health of the individual patient is still the doctor's primary concern the emphasis in medical practice has swung from the cure to the prevention of disease and from the protection of the individual to the protection of the community. The seventeenth century was an early stage in this transition.

Bibliography

(Books published or reprinted in the twentieth century)

General

Ackerknecht, E. H. (1955). *A Short History of Medicine*, paperback edn. 1982. Baltimore: Johns Hopkins University Press.

Beier, L. M. (1987). *Sufferers and Healers: the experience of illness in seventeenth-century England*. London: Routledge & Kegan Paul.

Cartwright, F. F (1977). *A Social History of Medicine*. Harlow: Longman.

Clendening, L. (1942). *Source Book of Medical History*. paperback edn. 1960. New York: Dover.

Debus, A. G. (ed.) (1974). *Medicine in Seventeenth Century England* Berkeley: University of California Press.

French, R & Wear, A. (eds) (1989). *The Medical Revolution of the Seventeenth Century*. Cambridge: University Press.

Garrison, F. H. (1913). *An Introduction to the History of Medicine*. 4th edn. 1929. Philadelphia: Saunders.

Guthrie, D. (1945). *A History of Medicine*. London: Nelson.

Jameson, E. (1961). *The Natural History of Quackery*. London: Joseph.

Porter, R. (1987). *Disease, Medicine and Society in England 1550–1860*. Basingstoke: Macmillan.

Singer, C. (1928). *A Short History of Medicine*, reprinted 1944. Oxford: Clarendon.

Thompson, C. J. S. (1961). *The Quacks of Old London*. London: Brentano.

Webster, C. (1975). *The Great Instauration: Science, medicine and reform 1626–1660*. London: Duckworth.

Wrigley, E. A. & Schofield, R. S. (1981). *The Population History of England 1541–1871*. London: Arnold.

Biography

Aubrey, J. (1680). *Brief Lives*, ed. by Barber, R. 1975. London: Folio Society.

Dewhurst, K. (1966). *Dr Thomas Sydenham*. London: Wellcome Historical Medical Library.

Finch, J. S. (1961). *Sir Thomas Browne: a doctor's life of science and faith*. New York: Collier.

Frank, R. G. Jnr. (1980). *Harvey and the Oxford Physiologists*. Berkeley: University of California Press.

Keele, K. D. (1965). *William Harvey: the man, the physician, and the scientist*. London: Nelson.

Keynes, Sir G. (1966). *The Life of William Harvey*. Oxford: Clarendon.

More, L. T. (1944). *The Life and Work of the Honourable Robert Boyle*. London: Oxford University Press.

Poynter, F. N. L. & Bishop, J. W. (1951). *A Seventeenth Century Doctor and his Patients: John Symcotts 1592?–1662*. Streatly: Bedfordshire Historical Record Society.

Translations and reprints

Browne, Sir T. (1653). *Religio medici*, Everyman edn. 1906. London: Dent.

Burton, R. (1621). *The Anatomy of Melancholy*, Everyman edn. 1932. London: Dent.

Fulton, J. F. (1930). *Selected Readings in the History of Physiology*. London: Baillière, Tindall & Cox.

Harvey, W. (1616). *The Anatomical Lectures of William Harvey*, edited and translated by Whitteridge, G. (1964). Edinburgh: Livingstone.

Harvey, W. (1625). *De motu cordis et sanguinis in animalibus*, translated by Franklin, K. J. (1957). Oxford: Blackwell.

Harvey, W. (1647). *De generatione animalium*, translated by Whitteridge, G. (1981). Oxford: Blackwell.

Hippocrates (4th century BC). *The Genuine Works of Hippocrates*, translated by Adams, F. (1849), reprinted 1938. Baltimore: Williams & Wilkins.

Lower, R. (1669). *Tractatus de corde*, translated by Franklin, K. J. (1932). London: Dawsons.

Lower, R. (1672). *De catarrhis*, translated by Hunter, R. & Macalpine, I. (1963). London: Dawsons.

Major, R. H. (1932). *Classic Descriptions of Disease*, 3rd edn. 1945. Springfield: Thomas.

Mayow, J. (1674). *Tractatus quinque medico-physici*, translated for the Alembic Club (1957). Edinburgh: Livingstone.

Sydenham, T. (1666). *Methodus curandi febres*, translated by Latham, R. G. (1848), reprinted 1987. Folkestone: Winterdown.

Woodall, J. (1617). *The Surgions Mate*, reprinted 1978. Bath: Kingsmead.

Medicine and pharmacy

Bloom, J. H. & James, R. R. (1935). *Medical Practitioners in the Diocese of London 1529–1725*. Cambridge: University Press.

Clark, Sir G. (1964). *A History of the Royal College of Physicians of London*, vol. 1. Oxford: Clarendon.

Cook, H. J. (1986). *The Decline of the Old Medical Regime in Stuart London*. Ithaca: Cornell University Press.

Copeman, W. S. C. (1967). *A History of the Worshipful Society of Apothecaries of London 1617–1967*. London: Pergamon.

Macdonald, M. (1981). *Mystical Bedlam: madness, anxiety and healing in seventeenth-century England*. Cambridge: University Press.

Matthews, L. G. (1962). *History of Pharmacy in Britain*. Edinburgh: Livingstone.

Pechey, J. (1694). *The English Herbal of Physical Plants*, abridged edn. 1951. London: Medical Publications.

Wall, C., Cameron, H. C., & Underwood, E. A. (1963). *A History of the Worshipful Society of the Apothecaries of London*, vol. 1. London: Oxford University Press.

Watson, G. (1966). *Theriac and Mithridatium*. London: Wellcome Historical Medical Library.

Surgery, midwifery and nursing

Cutter, I. S. & Viets, H. R. (1964). *A Short History of Midwifery*. Philadephia: Saunders.

Dobson, J. & Walker, R. M. (1979). *Barbers and Barber-Surgeons of London*. Oxford: Blackwell.

Dolan, J. A. (1916). *Nursing in Society: a historical perspective*, 14th edn. 1978. Philadelphia: Saunders.

Donnison, J. (1977). *Midwives and Medical Men*. London: Heinemann.

Eccles, A. (1982). *Obstetrics and Gynaecology in Tudor and Stuart England*. London: Croom Helm.

Maltz, M. (1946). *Evolution of Plastic Surgery*. New York: Froben.

Meade, R. H. (1968). *An Introduction to the History of General Surgery*. Philadelphia: Saunders.

Power, Sir D. ' A . (1933). *A Short History of Surgery*. London: Bale, Sons & Danielsson.

Seymer, L. R. (1957). *A General History of Nursing*, 5th edn. London: Faber & Faber.

Spencer, H. R. (1927). *The History of British Midwifery from 1650 to 1880*. London: Bale, Sons & Danielsson.

Willughby, P. (1863). *Observations in Midwifery*, reprinted 1972. Wakefield: S. R.

Woodall, J. (1617). *The Surgions Mate*, reprinted 1978. Bath: Kingsmead.

Infectious diseases

Bell, W. G. (1924). *The Great Plague of London in 1665*, 2nd edn. 1951. London: Lane.

Creighton, C. (1891, 1894). *A History of Epidemics in Britain*, 2 vols., reprinted 1965. Cambridge: University Press.

Decker, T. (1603). *The Wonderful Year 1603*. reprinted 1989. London: Folio Socirty.

Gale, A. H. (1959). *Epidemic Diseases*. Harmondsworth: Penguin.

Hirst, L. F. (1953). *The Conquest of Plague*. Oxford: Clarendon.

Lessor, J. (1962). *The Plague and the Fire*. London: Pan.

Shrewsbury, J. F. D. (1970). *A History of Bubonic Plague in the British Isles*. Cambridge: University Press.

Slack, P. (1985). *The Impact of Plague in Tudor and Stuart England*. London: Routledge & Kegan Paul.

References

Chapter 1. The pattern of English Medicine

1. Pelling, M. & Webster, C. (1979). Medical practitioners. In Webster, C. (ed.), *Health, Medicine and Mortality in the Sixteenth Century*, pp. 165–235. Cambridge: University Press.
2. Bloom, J. H. & James, R. R. (1935). *Medical Practitioners in the Diocese of London under the Act of Henry VIII c. 11*. Cambridge: University Press.
3. Raach, J. H. (1962). *A Directory of English Country Physicians 1603–1643*. London: Dawsons.
4. Allen, P. (1946). Medical education in seventeenth-century England. *J. Hist. Med.* **1**. 115–143.
5. Cook, H. J. (1986). *The Decline of the Old Medical Regime in Stuart London*. p. 254. Ithaca: Cornell University Press.
6. Clark, G. (1964). *A History of the Royal College of Physicians of London*, vol. 1, p. 133. Oxford: Clarendon.
7. *Ibid.*, p. 231.
8. Elmer, P. (1989). Medicine, religion and the puritan revolution. In French, R. & Wear, A. (eds.) *The Medical Revolution of the Seventeenth Century*, p. 43. Cambridge: University Press.
9. Barrett, C. R. B. (1905). *The History of the Society of Apothecaries of London*, p. xxvi. London: Elliot Stock.
10. *Ibid.*, p. 19.
11. Copeman, W. S. C. (1967). *The Worshipful Society of Apothecaries of London*, p. 44. London: Pergamon.
12. Barrett, C. R. B. (1905). *Op. cit.*, p. 6.
13. Clark, G. (1966). *A History of the Royal College of Physicians of London*, vol. 2, p. 433. Oxford: Clarendon.
14. Copeman, W. S. C. (1967). *Op. cit.*, p. 47.
15. Dobson, J. & Walker, R. M. (1979). *Barbers and Barber-Surgeons of London*, p. 47. Oxford: Blackwell.
16. *Ibid.*, p. 55.
17. Pelling, M. & Webster, C. (1979). *Op. cit.*
18. Donnison, J. (1977). *Midwives and Medical Men*, p. 4 London: Heinemann.
19. *Ibid.*, p. 8.
20. Aveling, J. H. (1875). *Memorials of Harvey*, p. 20. London: Churchill.

21. Guthrie, L. (1913). The Lady Sedley's receipt book, 1686, and other seventeenth-century receipt books. Proc. roy. Soc. Med. **6** 150–170.

22. Payne, J. F. (1900). *Thomas Sydenham*, p. 167. London: Fisher Unwin.

23. Webster, C. (1975). *The Great Instauration*, p. 260. London: Duckworth.

24. Beier, L. M. (1987). *Sufferers and Healers*, p. 159. London: Routledge & Kegan Paul.

25. Matthews, L. G. (1964). Licensed moutenbanks in Britain. *J. Hist. Med.* **19**, 30–45.

26. Thompson, C. J. S. (1928). *The Quacks of Old London*, p. 86. London: Brentano.

27. *Ibid.*, p. 219.

28. Keevil, J. J. (1957). The seventeenth-century English medical background. *Bull. Hist. Med.* **31**, 408–424.

29. Allderidge, P. (1979). In Webster, C. (1975). *Op. cit.*, pp. 141–164.

30. Hirst, L. F. (1953). *The Conquest of Plague*, p. 411. Oxford: Cavendish.

Chapter 2. Brief lives of some physicians

1. Birken, W (1987). The social problem of the English physician in the early seventeenth century. *Med. Hist.*, **31**. 201–216.

2. Aubrey, J. (1680). In Barber, R. (ed.) (1975). *Brief Lives*, p. 137. London: Folio Society.

3. Power, D'Arcy (1897). *William Harvey*, p. 26. London: Fisher Unwin.

4. Keynes, G. (1966). *The Life of William Harvey*, p. 53. Oxford: Clarendon.

5. Power, D'Arcy (1897). *Op. cit.*, p. 100.

6. Keynes, J. (1966). *Op. cit.*, p. 294.

7. *Ibid.*, p. 295.

8. Aubrey, J. (1680). *Op. cit.*, p. 139.

9. Power, D'Arcy (1897). *Op. cit.*, p. 160.

10. Payne, L. M. (1957). Sir Charles Scarburgh's Harveian Oration, 1662. *J. Hist. Med.* **12**, 158–164.

11. Munk, W. (1878). *The Roll of the Royal College of Physicians of London*, vol. 1, 2nd edn., p. 218. London: The College.

12. *Ibid.*, p. 220.

13. Glisson, F. (1650). *De rachitide*. English translation by Armin, P. (1651) p. 12. London: Cole.

14. Keevil, J. J. (1954). The illness of Charles, Duke of Albany (Charles I) from 1600 to 1612. *J. Hist. Med.*, **9**, 407–418.

15. Glisson, F. (1650). *Op. cit.*, p. 318.

16. Munk, W. (1878). *Op. cit.*, p. 338.

17. Dewhurst, K. (1964). *Thomas Willis as a Physician*, p. 9. Los Angeles: University of California Press.

18. *Ibid.*, p. 3.

19. Munk, W. (1878). *Op. cit.*, p. 341.

20. Dewhurst, K. (1964). *Op. cit.*, p. 12.

21. Creighton, C. (1894). *A History*

of Epidemics in Britain, vol. 1.
p. 550. Cambridge: Cambridge
University Press.

22. Willis, T. (1659). *Diatribe duae
medico-philosophiae*, p. 216
London: Martin, Allestry &
Dicas.

23. Willis, T. (1697). *Pharmaceutica
rationalis*, p. 80. London: Dring,
Harper & Leigh.

24. Franklin, A. W. (1974). Clinical
medicine. In Debus, A. G. (ed.)
*Medicine in Seventeenth Century
England*, pp. 113–145. Berkeley:
University of California.

25. Munk, W. (1878). *Op. cit.*,
p. 339.

26. *Ibid.*, p. 164.

27. *Ibid.*, p. 167.

28. Vigne, R. (1986). Mayerne and
his successors: some Huguenot
physicians under the Stuarts.
J. roy. Coll. Physns. **20**, 222–226.

29. Mayerne, T. T. de (1634–49).
Casebook. MS 444, Roy. Coll.
Physns.

30. Mayerne, T. T. de (1677).
Medicinal Councels or Advices, ed.
Shirley, T. p. 7. London: Ponder.

31. Palmer, R. (1733). *The Life of
the Most Eminent Baldwin Hamey*,
p. 4 MS 337 Roy. Coll. Physns.

32. *Ibid.*, p. 14.

33. Munk, W. (1878). *Op. cit.*,
p. 209.

34. Palmer, R. (1733). *Op. cit.*, p. 92

35. Blomberg, W. N. (1739). *An
Account of the Life and Writings of
Edmund Dickinson, MD, Physician
in Ordinary to King Charles II and
King James II*, p. 10. London:
Montagu.

36. *Ibid.*, p. 194

37. Munk, W. (1878). *Op. cit.*,
p. 394.

38. Blomberg, W. N. (1739). *Op.
cit.*, p. 106.

39. Dewhurst, K. (1966). *Dr Thomas
Sydenham*, p. vii. London:
Wellcome Historical Medical
Library.

40. Payne, J. F. (1900). *Thomas
Sydenham*, p. 56. London: Fisher
Unwin.

41. Sydenham, T. (1763). *The Entire
Works of Dr Thomas Sydenham*,
translated by Swan, J., 4th edn.,
p. 1. London: Cave

42. Payne, J. F. (1900). *Op. cit.*,
p. 153.

43. *Ibid.*, p. 214.

44. *Ibid.*, p. 7.

45. Sydenham, T. (1696). *The Whole
Works of that Excellent Practical
Physician, Dr Thomas Sydenham*,
translated by Pechey, J. (1722),
8th edn., p. 189. London:
Butterworth & Clay.

46. Payne, J. F. (1900). *Op. cit.*,
p. 149.

47. Sydenham, T. (1696). *Op. cit.*,
p. 390.

48. *Ibid.*, p. 410.

49. *Ibid.*, p. 447.

50. Poynter F. N. L. & Bishop,
J. W. (1951). *A Seventeenth
Century Doctor and his Patients:
John Symcotts, 1592?–1662*, p. xiii.
Streatly: Beds. Hist. Records Soc.

51. *Ibid.*, p. 13.

52. *Ibid.*, p. 11.

53. *Ibid.*, p. 49.

54. *Ibid.*, p. 50.

55. *Ibid.*, pp. 30, 31.

56. *Ibid.*, p. 46.

57. *Ibid.*, p. 103.

58. *Ibid.*, p. 34.

59. Finch, J. S. (1961). *Sir Thomas Browne: A Doctor's Life of Science and Faith*, p. 31. New York: Collier.
60. Munk, W. (1878). *Op. cit.*, p. 324.
61. Browne, T. (1635). *Religio medici*, ed. Rhys, E. (1906), P. 6 London: Dent.
62. *Ibid.*, p. 34.
63. Finch, J. S. (1961). *Op. cit.*, p. 132.

64. *Ibid.*, p. 163.
65. Townsend, G. L. (1967). Sir John Floyer (1649–1743) and his study of pulse and respiration. *J. Hist. Med.* **22**, 286–316.
66. Floyer, J. (1698). *A Treatise of the Asthma*, p. 37. London: Wilkin.
67. *Ibid.*, p. 108.
68. *Ibid.*, p. 169.
69. Townsend, G. L. (1967). *Op. cit.*

Chapter 3. The legacy of earlier medicine

1. Garrison, F. H. (1929). *An Introduction to the History of Medicine*, 4th edn., p. 23. Philadelphia: Saunders.
2. Major, R. H. (1954). *A History of Medicine*, p. 28. Oxford: Blackwell.
3. *Ibid.*, p. 50.
4. Stodola, J. & Volak J. (1984). *The Illustrated Book of Herbs*, ed. Bunney, S., p. 75. London: Octopus.
5. Russell, B. (1964). *History of Western Philosophy*, p. 74. London: George Allen & Unwin.
6. Singer, C. (1928). *A Short History of Medicine*, p. 34. Oxford: Clarendon.
7. Phillips, E. D. (1973). *Greek Medicine*, p. 26. London: Thames & Hudson.
8. Hippocrates (4th century BC). *The Genuine Works of Hippocrates*, translated by Adams, F. (1849), reprinted 1938, p. 355. Baltimore: Williams & Wilkins.
9. *Ibid.*, p. 299.
10. Guthrie, D. (1945). *A History of Medicine*, p. 54. Edinburgh: Nelson.
11. Hippocrates. *Op. cit.*, p. 112.
12. *Ibid.*, p. 44.
13. Phillips, E. D. (1973). *Op. cit.*, p. 144.
14. Scarborough, J. (1969). *Roman Medicine*, p. 43. London: Thames & Hudson.
15. Singer, C. (1928). *Op. cit.*, p. 43.
16. Brain, P. (1986). *Galen on Bloodletting*, p. 14. Cambridge: Cambridge University Press.
17. Watson, G. (1966). *Theriac and Mithridatium*, p. 121. London: Wellcome Historical Medical Library
18. *Ibid.*, p. 37.
19. *Ibid.*, p. 42.
20. Amulree, Lord (1973). Hygienic conditions in ancient Rome and in modern London. *Med. Hist.*, **17**, 244–255.
21. Major, R. H. (1945). *Classic Descriptions of Disease*, 3rd edn., p. 197. Springfield: Thomas.
22. Major, R. H. (1954). *Op. cit.*, p. 235.

23. Osler, W. (1921). *The Evolution of Modern Medicine*, p. 98. New Haven: Yale University Press.

24. Major, R. H. (1954). *Op. cit.*, p. 284.

25. Rubin, S. (1974). *Medieval English Medicine*, p. 59. Newton Abbot: David & Charles.

26. Cartwright, F. F. (1977). *A Social History of Medicine*, p. 29. London: Longman.

27. Munger, R. S. (1949). Guiaum the holy wood from the New World. *J. Hist. Med.*, **4**, 196–229.

28. Major, R. H. (1954). *Op. cit.*, p. 378.

29. Sherrington, C. (1946). *The Endeavour of Jean Fernel*, p. 101. Cambridge: Cambridge University Press.

30. *Ibid.*, p. 100. Quoted from Plancy (1607), Life of Fernel.

31. Pagel, W. (1928). *Paracelsus: An Introduction to Philosophical Medicine in the Era of the Renaissance*, 2nd edn., p. 13. Basel: Karger.

32. *Ibid.*, p. 129.

33. *Ibid.*, p. 145.

34. Wightman, W. P. D. (1971). *The Emergence of Scientific Medicine*, p. 43, Edinburgh: Oliver & Boyd.

35. Finch, J. S. (1961). *Sir Thomas Browne: A Doctor's Life of Science and Faith*, p. 57. New York: Collier.

36. Major R. H. (1954). *Op. cit.*, p. 553.

37. Slack, P. (1985). *The Impact of Plague in Tudor and Stuart England*, pp. 61, 62. London: Routledge & Kegan Paul.

38. Sloan, A. W. (1971). The sweating sickness in England. *S. Afr. med. J.*, **45**, 473–475.

39. Soranzo, G. (1554). In *Cal. State Papers (Venetian)*, translated and edited by Cavendish-Bentinck, G. (1873). vol. 5, p. 541. London: Public Record Office.

40. Copeman, W. S. C. (1960). *Doctors and Disease in Tudor Times*, p. 117. London: Dawson.

41. Bonner, J. T. (1951). The horn of the unicorn. *Sci. Amer.*, **184** (3): 42–43.

42. Copeman, W. S. C. (1960). *Op. cit.*, p. 20.

43. *Ibid.*, p. 23.

44. Boorde, A. (1547). *The Breviary of Helthe*, p. 4. London: Middleton.

45. *Ibid.*, pp. 88, 91.

46. Phaire, T. (1545). *The Boke of Chyldren*, reprinted 1955, pp. 22ff. Edinburgh: Livingstone.

47. *Ibid.*, p. 13.

48. Clark, G. (1964). *A History of the Royal College of Physicians of London*, vol. 1, p. 55. Oxford: Clarendon.

49. *Ibid.*, p. 101.

Chapter 4. The practice of medicine

1. Gale, A. H. (1959). *Epidemic Diseases*, p. 52 Harmondsworth: Penguin.

2. Cartwright, F. F. (1977). *A Social History of Medicine*, p. 116. London: Longman.

3. Clark, G. (1964). *A History of the Royal College of Physicians of*

London, vol. 1, p. 178. Oxford: Clarendon.

4. Fletcher, J. (1641). *The Different Causes and Judgments of Urine*, preface. London: Legatt.

5. Primrose, J. (1651). *The Errours of the People in Physick*, translated by Wilkie, R., p. 65. London: Bourne.

6. Andrews, W. (1656). *The Astrological Physitian*, p. 11. London: Sawbridge.

7. Culpeper, N. (1653). *The English Physitian Enlarged*, p. 55. London: Cole.

8. Chapman, A. (1979). Astrological medicine. In Webster, C. (ed.) *Health, Medicine and Mortality in the Sixteenth Century*, pp. 275–300. Cambridge: Cambridge Univeristy Press.

9. Sydenham. T. (1696). *The Whole Works of that Excellent Practical Physician, Dr Thomas Sydenham*, translated by Pechey, J. 8th edn. (1722). p. 37. London: Bettesworth & Clay.

10. Barbette, P. (1675). *The Practice of the Most Successful Physician, Paul Barbette*, p. 17. London: Brome.

11. Barrough, P. (1617). *The Method of Physick*, 5th edn. p. 31. London: Field.

12. *Ibid.*, p. 34.

13. Floyer, J. (1698). *A Treatise of the Asthma*, p. 10. London: Martin, Allestry & Dicas.

14. Garrison, F. H. (1929). *An Introduction to the History of Medicine*, p. 71. Philadelphia: Saunders.

15. *Ibid.*, p. 582.

16. Barrough, P. (1617). *Op. cit.*, p. 40.

17. Bruel, W. (1632). *The Physicians Practice*, p. 58. London: Shears.

18. *Ibid.*, p. 57.

19. Sydenham, T. (1696). *Op. cit.*, p. 341.

20. *Ibid.*, p. 343.

21. *Ibid.*, p. 190.

22. *Ibid.*, p. 191.

23. *Ibid.*, p. 417.

24. Major, R. H. (1945). *Classic Descriptions of Disease*, 3rd edn., p. 585. Springfield: Thomas.

25. Willis, T. (1684). *Practice of Physick*, translated by Pondage, S., Part IX (2), p. 175. London: Dring, Harper & Leigh.

26. Bruel, W. (1632). *Op. cit.*, p. 329.

27. Barrough, P. (1617). *Op. cit.*, p. 162.

28. *Ibid.*, p. 363.

29. Sydenham, T. (1696), *Op. cit.*, pp. 249–250.

30. *Ibid.*, p. 251.

31. Barrough, P. (1617). *Op. cit.*, pp. 132–133.

32. Brown, J. (1858). *Horae subsecivae*, 1st series, 3rd edn. (1897), p. 54. London: Black.

33. Keele, K. D. (1965). *William Harvey, the Man, the Physician, and the Scientist*, p. 80. London: Nelson.

34. Sydenham, T. (1696). *Op. cit.*, p. 72.

35. Cole, W. (1689). *A Physico-Medical Essay Concerning the late Frequency of Apoplexies*, p. 174. Oxford: publisher unspecified.

36. Harvey, G. (1689). *The Art of Curing Diseases by Expectation*, p. 5. London: Partridge.

37. Barbette, P. (1675). *Op. cit.*, p. 192.
38. Floyer, J. (1698). *Op. cit.*, p. 108.
39. Sydenham, T. (1696). *Op. cit.*, p. 17.
40. *Ibid.*, p. 32.
41. *Ibid.*, p. 24.
42. *Ibid.*, p. 233.
43. *Ibid.*, p. 358.
44. *Ibid.*, p. 210
45. Pechey, J. (1694). *The English Herbal of Physical Plants*, abridged edn. (1951), p. 5. London: Medical Publications.
46. Willis, T. (1684). *Op. cit.*, Part VIII, p. 18.
47. Barrough, P. (1617). *Op. cit.*, p. 41.
48. Willis, T. (1684). *Op. cit.*, p. 81
49. Sakula, A. (1988). A history of asthma. *J. roy. Coll. Physns. London*, **22**, 36–44.
50. Poynter, F. N. L. & Bishop, J. W. (1951). *Op. cit.*, p. 107.
51. *Ibid.*, p. 85.
52. *Ibid.*, p. 96.
53. Biggs, N. (1651). *The Vanity of the Craft of Physick*, p. 6. London: Blackmore.
54. *Ibid.*, pp. 97, 103.
55. Primrose, J. (1651). *Op. cit.*, p. 141.
56. Coley, N. G. (1979). 'Cures without care', chymical physicians and mineral waters in seventeenth-century English medicine. *Med. Hist.* **23**, 191–214.
57. Sydenham, T. (1696). *Op. cit.*, p. 377.
58. *Ibid.*, p. 190.
59. Radhill, S. X. (1974). Pediatrics. In Debus, A. G. (ed.) *Medicine in Seventeenth Century England*, pp. 237–282. Berkeley: University of California.
60. Pechey, J. (1697). *A General Treatise of the Diseases of Infants and Children*, p. 7. London: Wellington.
61. Radbill, S. X. (1974). *Op. cit.*, p. 252.
62. Harris, W. (1689). *A Treatise of the Acute Diseases of Infants*, English translation by Martyn, J. (1742), p. 24. London: Astley.
63. *Ibid.*, pp. 74, 107.
64. Pemell, R. (1653). *A Treatise of the Diseases of Children*, p. 7. London: Stephens.
65. Still, G. F. (1931). *The History of Paediatrics*, p. 238. London: Oxford University Press.
66. Pechey, J. (1697). *A General Treatise of the Diseases of Infants and Children*, p. 152. London: Wellington.
67. Willis, T. (1672). *Two Discourses Concerning the Soul of Brutes*, translated by Pordage, S. (1683), p. 215. London: Dring & Leigh.
68. Dewhurst, K. (1964). *Thomas Willis as a Physician*, p. 7. Los Angeles: University of California.
69. Barrough, P. (1617). *Op. cit.*, p. 44
70. *Ibid.*, p. 45.
71. Sydenham, T. (1696). *Op. cit.*, p. 305.
72. MacDonald, M. (1981). *Mystical Bedlam*, p. 130. Cambridge: Cambridge University Press.
73. *Ibid.*, p. 4.
74. Burton, R. (1621). *The Anatomy of Melancholy*, Everyman edn. (1932), vol. 1, P. 20. London: Dent.
75. *Ibid.*, p. 399.

76. MacDonald, M. (1981). *Op. cit.*, pp. 35, 199.

77. *Ibid.*, p. 148.

Chapter 5. Medical science

1. Garrison, F. H. (1929). *An Introduction to the History of Medicine*, 4th edn., p. 137. Philadelphia: Saunders.

2. Singer, C. (1941). *A Short History of Science*, p. 234. Oxford: Clarendon.

3. Major, R. H. (1954). *A History of Medicine*, vol. 1, p. 176. Oxford: Blackwell.

4. Singer, C. (1950). *A History of Biology*, revised edn., p. 174. New York: Schuman.

5. Clark, G. (1964). *A History of the Royal College of Physicians of London*, vol. 1, p. 160. Oxford: Clarendon.

6. Young, J. (1929). Malpighi's 'De Pulmonibus'. *Proc. roy. Soc. Med.*, **23**, 1–14.

7. Raven, C. E. (1950). *John Ray, Naturalist*, p. 144. Cambridge: Cambridge University Press.

8. Pechey, J. (1694). *The English Herbal of Physical Plants*, abridged edn. (1951), p. 5. London: Medical Publications.

9. Major, R. H. (1954). *Op. cit.*, p. 143.

10. Guthrie, D. (1945). *A History of Medicine*, p. 64. London: Nelson.

11. Singer, C. (1957). *A Short History of Anatomy and Physiology from the Greeks to Harvey*, 2nd edn., p. 57. New York: Dover.

12. *Ibid.*, p. 76.

13. *Ibid.*, p. 121.

14. *Ibid.*, p. 131.

15. *Ibid.*, p. 134.

16. Singer, C. (1928). *A Short History of Medicine*, reprinted 1944, p. 110. Oxford: Clarendon.

17. Valadez, F. (1974). Anatomical studies at Oxford and Cambridge. In Debus, A. G. (ed.) *Medicine in Seventeenth Century England*, pp. 393–420. Berkeley: University of California Press.

18. Power, D'Arcy (1897). *William Harvey*, pp. 48–49. London: Fisher Unwin.

19. Harvey, W. (1616). *The Anatomical Lectures of William Harvey*, edited and translated by Whitteridge, G. (1964), p. 17. Edinburgh: Livingstone.

20. Valadez, F. (1974). *Op. cit.*,

21. Lower, R. (1669). *Tractatus de corde*, translated by Franklin, K. J. (1932). p. 31. London: Dawsons.

22. Lower, R. (1672). *De catarrhis*, translated by Hunter, R. & Macalpine, I. (1963), pp. 6–8. London: Dawsons.

23. Valadez, F. (1974). *Op. cit.*,

24. Keele, K. D. (1974). Physiology. In Debus, A. G. (ed.), *Op. cit.*, pp. 147–181.

25. Singer, C. (1928). *Op. cit.*, p. 38.

26. *Ibid.*, p. 56.

27. *Ibid.*, p. 58.

28. *Ibid.*, p. 108.

29. Major, R. H. (1954). *Op. cit.*, p. 486.

30. Foster, M. G. (1901). *Lectures on the History of Physiology*, p. 75. Cambridge: Cambridge University Press.

31. *Ibid.*, p. 136.

32. Franklin, K. J. (1949). *A Short History of Physiology*, 2nd edn., p. 68. London: Staples Press.

33. *Ibid.*, p. 69.

34. Dodds, C. (1958). Harvey, scientist and physician. In McMichael, J. (ed.), *Circulation*, pp. 27–30. Oxford: Blackwell.

35. Harvey, W. (1628). *De motu cordis et sanguinis in animalibus*, translated by Franklin, K. J. (1957), p. 19. Oxford: Blackwell.

36. *Ibid.*, translated by Willis, R. (1847). In Boylan, J. W. (ed.). *Founders of Experimental Physiology*, p. 93. Munich: Lehmanns.

37. *Ibid.*, translated by Franklin, K. J. (1957), p. 62.

38. *Ibid.*, translated by Willis, R. (1847), p. 111.

39. Willis, T. (1664). *Cerebri anatome*, pp. 99–108. London: Martyn & Allestry.

40. Lower, R. (1669). *Tractatus de corde*, translated by Franklin, K. J., (1932), p. 189. London: Dawsons.

41. *Ibid.*, pp. 166–169.

42. Mayow, J. (1674). *Tractatus quinque medico-physici*, translated for the Alembic Club (1957), pp. 101–103. Edinburgh: Livingstone.

43. *Ibid.*, p. 201.

44. *Ibid.*, p. 249.

45. Glisson, F. (1677). De ventriculo et intestinis. In Fulton,

J. F. (1930). *Selected Readings in the History of Physiology*, pp. 199–292. London: Baillière, Tindall & Cox.

46. More, L. T. (1944). *The Life and Work of the Honourable Robert Boyle*, pp. 241, 242. London: Oxford University Press.

47. Hooke, R. (1667). An account of an experiment made by M. Hook of preserving animals alive by blowing through their lungs with bellows. *Phil. Trans. Roy. Soc.* 2, 539–540.

48. Brock, A. J. (1929). *Greek Medicine*, pp. 108–110. London: Dent.

49. Meyer, A. W. (1939). *The Rise of Embryology*, p. 26. London: Oxford University Press.

50. Fabricius, H. (1600, 1621). *The Embryological Treatises of Hieronymus Fabricius of Aquapendente*, translated by Adelmann, H. B. (1942), p. 259. Ithaca, New York: Cornell University Press.

51. Singer, C. (1950). *Op. cit.*, p. 460.

52. Bodemer, C. W. (1974). Materialistic and neoplatonic influences in embryology. In Debus, A. G. (ed.). *Op. cit.*, pp. 183–213.

53. Cole, F. J. (1957). Harvey's animals *J. Hist. Med.* 12, 106–113.

54. Franklin, K. J. (1961). *William Harvey, Englishman*, p. 107. London: MacGibbon & Kee.

55. Bodemer, C. W. (1974). *Op. cit.*

56. Harvey, W. (1847). *De generatione animalium*, translated by Whitteridge, G. (1981), p. 332. Oxford: Blackwell.

57. Keynes, G. (1960). *The Life of*

William Harvey, p. 349. Oxford: Clarendon.
58. Bodemer, C. W. (1974), *Op. cit.*
59. Heberden, W. (ed.) (1759). *A Collection of the Yearly Bills of Mortality*, pp. 7–9. London: Miller.
60. Cassedy, J. H. (1974). Medicine and the rise of statistics. In Debus, A. G. (ed.) *Op. cit.*, pp. 283–312.
61. *Idem.*
62. Graunt, J. (1662). *Natural and Political Observations on the Bills of Mortality*, reprinted 1759, p. 10. London: Miller.
63. *Ibid.*, p. 17.
64. Rosen, G. (1953). Economic and social policy in the development of public health. *J. Hist. Med.* **8**, 406–430.
65. Glass, D. V. (1946). Gregory King and the population of England and Wales at the end of the seventeenth century. *Eugen. Rev.* **37**, 170–183.
66. *Idem.*

Chapter 6. The apothecary

1. Kremers, E. & Urdang, G. (1976). *History of Pharmacy*, 4th edn., revised by Sonnedecker, G., p. 20. Philadelphia: Lippincott.
2. Watson, G. (1966). *Theriac and Mithridatium*, p. 100. London: Wellcome Historical Medical Library.
3. Kremers, E. & Urdang, G. (1976). *Op. cit.*, p. 27.
4. *Ibid.*, p. 100.
5. Watson, G. (1966). *Op. cit.*, p. 114.
6. Matthews, L. G. (1962). *History of Pharmacy in Britain*, pp. 37, 38. Edinburgh: Livingstone.
7. Burnby, J. G. L. (1983). *A Study of the English Apothecary from 1660 to 1760*, pp. 13,16. London: Wellcome Institute for the History of Medicine.
8. Kremers, E. & Urdang, G. (1976). *Op. cit.*, p. 101.
9. Matthews, L. G. (1965). Herbals and formularies. In Poynter, F. N. L. (ed.). *The Evolution of Pharmacy in Britain*, pp. 187–213. London: Pitman.
10. Barrett, C. R. B. (1905). *The History of the Society of Apothecaries of London*, p. xvi. London: Elliot Stock.
11. Cope, Z. (1956). Influence of the Society of Apothecaries on medical education. *Brit. med. J.*, **i**, 1–6.
12. Barrett, C. R. B. (1905). *Op. cit.*, pp. xxvii–xxviii.
13. *Ibid.*, p. 2.
14. *Ibid.*, p. 23.
15. *Ibid.*, p. 6.
16. Dickinson, T. V. (1929). The armorial bearings of the Worshipful Society of Apothecaries. *Proc. roy. Soc. Med.* **23**, 11–14.
17. Barrett, C. R. B. (1905). *Op. cit.*, p. 86.
18. *Ibid.*, p. 119.
19. Wall, C., Cameron, H. C. & Underwood, E. A. (1963). *A*

History of the Worshipful Society of the Apothecaries of London, vol. 1, p. 168. London: Oxford University Press.

20. Copeman, W. S. C. (1967). *The Worshipful Society of Apothecaries of London*, p. 15. London: Pergamon.

21. Matthews, L. G. (1962). *Op. cit.*, p. 50

22. *Ibid.*, p. 51.

23. Barrett, C. R. B. (1965). *Op. cit.*, p. 13.

24. Matthews, L. G. (1962). *Op. cit.*, p. 210.

25. *Ibid.*, p. 211.

26. *Ibid.*, p. 241.

27. Burnby, J. G. L. (1983). *Op. cit.*, p. 89.

28. Underwood, E. A. (1950). Nicholas Culpeper. In *Chambers's Encyclopedia*, New edn., vol. 4, p. 292. London: Newnes.

29. Culpeper, N. (1683). *The London Dispensatory*, revised edn., p. 49. London: Sawbridge.

30. Matthews, L. G. (1962). *Op. cit.*, p. 322.

31. Burnby, J. G. L. (1983). *Op. cit.*, p. 92.

32. *Ibid.*, p. 89.

33. Wall, C. *et al.* (1963). *Op. cit.*, p. 112.

34. Matthews, L. G. (1962). *Op. cit.*, p. 112.

35 Boghurst W. (1666). Loimografia: An Acount of the Great Plague of London in the year 1665. Ed. Payne, J.F. 1894 *Transactions of the Epidemiological Society of London.* **13.** Supplement pp.1–99.

36. King, L. S. (1958). *The Medical World of the Eighteenth Century*, p. 18. Chicago: University of Chicago Press.

Chapter 7. Surgery

1. Guthrie, D. (1945). *A History of Medicine*, p. 6. Edinburgh: Nelson.

2. Major, R. H. (1954). *A History of Medicine*, p. 41. Springfield, Ill.: Thomas.

3. Garrison, F. H. (1929). *An Introduction to the History of Medicine*, p. 64. Philadelphia: Saunders.

4. *Ibid.*, p. 55.

5. Allbutt, T. C. (1905). *The Historical Relations of Medicine and Surgery to the End of the Sixteenth Century*, p. 5. London: Macmillan.

6. Singer, C. (1928). *A Short History of Medicine*, p. 43. Oxford: Clarendon.

7. Maltz, M. (1946). *The Evolution of Plastic Surgery*, p. 29. New York: Froben.

8. Shelley, H. S. (1958). Cutting for the stone. *J. Hist. Med.*, **13**, 50–67.

9. Tallmadge, G. K. (1946). Some anaesthetics of antiquity. *J. Hist. Med.*, **1**, 515–520.

10. Power, D'A (1933). *A Short History of Surgery*, p. 9. London: Bale, Sons & Danielsson.

11. Scarborough, J. (1968). Roman medicine and the legions: a

reconsideration. *Med. Hist.*, **12**, 254–261.

12. Bishop, W. J. (1960). *The Early History of Surgery*, p. 54. London: Hale.
13. Major, R. H. (1954). *Op. cit.*, pp. 250, 251.
14. Bishop, W. J. (1960). *Op. cit.*, p. 62.
15. Major, R. H. (1954). *Op. cit.*, p. 321.
16. *Ibid.*, pp. 310, 311.
17. Bishop, W. J. (1960). *Op. cit.*, p. 66.
18. *Ibid.*, p. 102.
19. *Ibid.*, p. 67.
20. *Ibid.*, pp. 79, 82.
21. Major, R. H. (1954). *Op. cit.*, pp. 428, 429.
22. Guthrie, D. (1945). *Op. cit.*, p. 453.
23. Meade, R. H. (1968). *An Introduction to the History of General Surgery*, p. 345. Philadelphia: Saunders.
24. Guthrie, D. (1945). *Op. cit.*, P. 148.
25. Bishop, W. J. (1960). *Op. cit.*, pp. 85, 86.
26. Vicary, T. (1586) (1st edn. 1548). *The Englishmans Treasure or Treasor for Englishmen: With the true Anatomye of Mans Body*, pp. 3–5. London: Perin.
27. Dobson, J.& Walker, R.M. (1979). *Barbers and Barber-Surgeons of London*, p. 24 Oxford: Blackwell.
28. *Ibid.*, p. 34.
29. *Ibid.*, p. 36.
30. *Ibid.*, p. 46.
31. *Ibid.*, p. 82.
32. *Ibid.*, p. 48.
33. Appleby, J. H. (1981). New light on John Woodall, surgeon and adventurer. *Med. Hist.* **25**, 251–268.
34. Woodall, J. (1617). *The Surgions Mate*, p. 184. London: Lisle
35. Woodall, J. (1639). *A Treatise . . . of that most fearefull and contagious Disease called the Plague*, published with 2nd edn. of *The Surgions Mate*, p. 367. London: Bourne.
36. Appleby, J. H. (1981). *Op. cit.*
37. Longmore, T. (1891). *Richard Wiseman: A Biographical Study*, p. 7. London: Longmans Green.
38. *Ibid.*, p. 113.
39. Wiseman, R. (1676). *Severall Chirurgicall Treatises*, p. 451. London: Royston & Took.
40. Wiseman, R. (1672). *A Treatise of Wounds*, p. A3. London: Royston.
41. Wiseman, R. (1676). *Op. cit.*, p. 247.
42. *Ibid.*, Treatise VIII, p. 3.
43. Beier, L. M. (1987). *Sufferers and Healers*, p. 52. London: Routledge & Kegan Paul.
44. Binns, J. (ND). *Surgical Casebook*, Sloane MS 153, pp. 2, 3. London: British Library.
45. *Ibid.*, p. 93
46. *Ibid.*, 173.
47. Beier, L. M. (1987). *Op. cit.*, p. 71.
48. Binns, J. (ND). *Op. cit.*, p. 172.
49. Beier, L. M. (1987). *Op. cit.*, p. 90.
50. Wiseman, R. (1676). *Op. cit.*, p. 349.
51. *Ibid.*, p. 406.
52. *Ibid.*, p. 371.
53. Meade, R. H. (1968). *Op. cit.*, p. 17.

54. Maltz, R. (1946). *Op. cit.*, p. 192.
55. Bonham, T. (1630). *The Chyrurgians Closet*, p. 4. London: Brewster.
56. Yonge, J. (1679). *Currus triumphalis è terebinthô*, pp. 110, 111. London: Martyn.
57. Meade, R. H. (1968). *Op. cit.*, p. 346.
58. Bankoff, G. (1947). *The Story of Surgery*, pp. 117, 118. London: Baker.
59. Meade, R. H. (1968). *Op. cit.*, p. 109.
60. Bishop, W. J. (1960). *Op. cit.*, p. 102.
61. Meade, R. H. (1968). *Op. cit.*, p. 186.
62. Sennert, D. (1646). *The Institutions or Fundamentals of the Whole Art both of Physick and Chirurgery*, translated by N. D. B. P. (1658), p. 327. London: Lloyd.
63. Horine, E. F. (1946). Episodes in the history of anaesthesia. *J. Hist. Med.*, **1**, 521–526.
64. Power, D'A. (1933). *Op. cit.*, p. 84.
65. Beier, L. M. (1987). *Op. cit.*, p. 12.

Chapter 8. Midwives and nurses

1. McKenzie, D. (1927). *The Infancy of Medicine*, p. 318. London: Macmillan.
2. Phillips, E. D. (1973). *Greek Medicine*, p. 112. London: Thames & Hudson.
3. *Ibid.*, p. 113.
4. *Ibid.*, p. 165.
5. Forbes, T. R. (1964). The regulation of English midwives in the sixteenth and seventeenth centuries. *Med. Hist.* **8**, 235–243.
6. Major, R. H. (1954). *A History of Medicine*, p. 436. Springfield, Ill.: Thomas.
7. Eccles, A. (1982). *Obstetrics and Gynaecology in Tudor and Stuart England*, p. 12. London: Croom Helm.
8. Rueff, J. (1636). *The Expert Midwife*, p. 40. London, S. B.
9. *Ibid*, p. 58.
10. *Ibid.*, p. 81.
11. *Ibid.*, pp. 104–108.
12. Sharp, J. (1671). *The Midwives Book*, p. 92. London: Miller.
13. *Ibid.*, p. 102.
14. *Ibid.*, p. 217.
15. *Ibid.*, p. 364.
16. Phillips, M. H. (1952). Percival Willughby's observations in midwifery. *J. Obs. Gyn. Brit. Emp.* **59**, 753–762.
17. Willughby, P. (1863). *Observations in Midwifery*, ed. by Blenkinsop, H., reprinted with introduction by Thornton, J. L. (1972), p. 21. Wakefield, S. R.
18. *Ibid.*, p. 27.
19. *Ibid.*, p. 56.
20. *Ibid.*, p. 241.
21. Spencer, H. R. (1927). *The History of British Midwifery from 1650 to 1800*, p. i. London: Bale, Sons & Danielsson.
22. *Ibid.*, p. xvi.
23. Cutter, I. S. & Viets,

H. R. (1964). *A Short History of Midwifery*, p. 52. Philadelphia: Saunders.

24. Barrough, P. (1617). *The Method of Physick*, p. 202, Publisher not stated.

25. *Ibid.*, p. 204.

26. Cutter, I. S. & Viets, H. R. (1964). *Op. cit.*, p. 11.

27. Sermon, W. (1671). *The Ladies Companion or the English Midwife*, p. 127. London: Thomas.

28. *Ibid.*, pp. 127–134.

29. *Ibid.*, p. 136.

30. Power, D'A. (1933). *A Short History of Surgery*, p. 60. London: Bale, Sons & Danielsson.

31. Pechey, J. (1698). *The Compleat Midwives Practice Enlarged*, pp. 113, 114. London: Rhodes.

32. Sermon, W. (1671) *Op. cit.*, p. 27

33. Mauriceau, F. (1668). *Des maladies des femmes grosses et accouchées*, translated by Chamberlen, H. (1673), p. 43. London: Darby.

34. Eccles, A. (1982). *Op. cit.*, p. 62.

35. Eshleman, M. K. (1975). Diet during pregnancy in the sixteenth and seventeenth centuries. *J. Hist. Med.* **30**, 23–39.

36. Rueff, J. (1636). *Op. cit.*, p. 163.

37. Mauriceau, F. (1668). *Op. cit.*, p. 216.

38. Rueff, J. (1636). *Op. cit.*, p. 101.

39. Mauriceau, F. (1668). *Op. cit.*, p. 216.

40. *Ibid.*, pp. 315, 316.

41. Willughby, P. (1863). *Op. cit.*, pp. 179, 199.

42. Eccles, A. (1982). *Op. cit.*, p. 80.

43. Sharp, J. (1671). *Op. cit.*, p. 350.

44. Mauriceau, F. (1668). *Op. cit.*, p. 365.

45. Sharp, J. (1671). *Op. cit.*, p. 339.

46. *Ibid.*, p. 357.

47. *Ibid.*, p. 293.

48. *Ibid.*, p. 300.

49. Rueff, J. (1636). *Op. cit.*, p. 88.

50. *Ibid.*, p. 14.

51. Wiseman, R. (1676). *Severall Chirurgicall Treatises*, p. 103. London: Royston & Took.

52. Sharp, J. (1671). *Op. cit.*, p. 257.

53. *Ibid.*, p. 260.

54. Pechey, J. (1698). *Op. cit.*, p. 228.

55. Dolan, J. A. (1978). *Nursing in Society*, 14th edn., p. 47. Philadelphia: Saunders.

56. Bullough, B. & Bullough V. L. (1964). *The Emergence of Modern Nursing*, p. 40. New York: Macmillan.

57. *Ibid.*, p. 43.

58. *Ibid.*, p. 46.

59. Seymer, L. R. (1957). *A General History of Nursing*, p. 44. London: Faber & Faber.

60. Dolan, J. A. (1978). *Op. cit.*, p. 68.

61. *Ibid.*, p. 91.

62. *Ibid.*, p. 94.

63. Bullough, B. & Bullough, V. R. (1964). *Op. cit.*, p. 61.

64. *Ibid.*, p. 66.

Chapter 9. Housewives, clergy and quacks

1. Hoby, M. (ND). *Diary of Lady Margaret Hoby 1599–1605*, ed. by Meads, D. M. (1930), p. 47. London: Routledge.

2. *Ibid.*, p. 100.

3. *Ibid.*, p. 168.
4. *Ibid.*, p. 184.
5. Grey, E. (1653). *A Choice Manuall or Rare and Select Secrets in Physick*, p. 54. London: Shears.
6. *Ibid.*, p. 70.
7. *Ibid.*, p. 9.
8. *Ibid.*, p. 13.
9. *Idem.*
10. *Ibid.*, p. 133.
11. *Ibid.*, p. 92.
12. *Ibid.*, p. 104.
13. Doggett, M. (1682). *Her Booke of Receits*, p. 8. Brit. Library.
14. *Ibid.*, p. 19.
15. *Ibid.*, p. 30.
16. Guthrie, L. (1913). The Lady Sedley's receipt book 1686 and other seventeenth-century receipt books. *Proc. Roy. Soc. Med.* **6**, Part 2 (History of Medicine), pp. 150–170.
17. Sedley, C. (1686). *Receipt Book*, p. 59. Roy. Coll. Physns. MS 534.
18. *Ibid.*, p. 40.
19. *Ibid.*, p. 57.
20. *Ibid.*, p. 34.
21. *Ibid.*, p. 17.
22. Ranelagh (ND). *My Lady Ranelagh's Choice Receipts*, pp.3, 56. Brit. Library Sloane MS 1367.
23. *Ibid.*, p. 15.
24. *Ibid.*, pp. 4, 10.
25. Sowerby, L. (1652). *The Ladies Dispensatory*, p. 9. London: Calvert.
26. *Ibid.*, p. 86.
27. *Ibid.*, p. 137.
28. *Ibid.*, p. 187.
29. *Ibid.*, p. 237.
30. Harvey, G. (1676). *The Family Physician and the House-Apothecary*, title page. London: T. R.
31. *Ibid.*, p. 143.
32. *Ibid.*, p. 154.
33. Harvey, G. (1689). *The Art of Curing Diseases by Expectation*, p. 5. London: Partridge.
34. MacDonald, M (1981). *Mystical Bedlam: madness, anxiety and healing in seventeenth-century England*, p. 20. Cambridge: Cambridge University Press.
35. *Ibid.*, p. 32.
36. Aubrey, J. (1680). *Brief Lives*, ed. by Barber, R. (1975), p. 226. London: Folio Society.
37. MacDonald, M. (1981). *Op. cit.*, p. 189.
38. *Ibid.*, p. 214.
39. Frank, R. G. Jnr. (1974). The John Ward diaries: mirror of seventeenth-century science and medicine. *J. Hist. Med.* **29**, 147–179.
40. Ward, J. (ND). *Diary 1648–1679*, ed. by Severn, C. (1839), p. 243. London: Colburn.
41. *Ibid.*, p. 251.
42. *Ibid.*, p. 291.
43. *Ibid.*, p. 237.
44. *Ibid.*, p. 95.
45. *Ibid.*, p. 242.
46. Bankoff, G. (1947). *The Story of Surgery*, p. 117. London: Baker.
47. Matthews, L. G. (1964). Licensed mountebanks in Britain. *J. Hist. Med*, **19**, 30–45.
48. Zimmerman, L. M. (1974). Surgery. In Debus, A. G. (ed.) *Medicine in Seventeenth Century England*, pp.49–69 Berkeley: University of California Press.
49. *Idem.*
50. Guthrie, D. (1949). *A History of*

Medicine, p. 15. Edinburgh: Nelson.

51. Digby, K. (1688). *Choice and Experimental Receipts in Physick and Chirurgery*, p. 25. London: publisher unknown.

52. *Ibid.*, p. 62.

53. *Ibid.*, p. 49.

54. *Ibid.*, p. 103.

55. *Ibid.*, pp. 163–167.

56. Laver, A. B. (1978). Miracles no wonder! The mesmeric phenomena and organic cures of Valentine Greatraks. *J. Hist. Med.* **33**, 35–46.

57. Hunter, R. A. & MacAlpine, I. (1956). Valentine Greatraks. *St Barts. Hosp. J.* **60**, 361–368.

58. Jameson, E. (1961). *The Natural History of Quackery*, p. 153. London: Joseph.

59. Matthews, L. G. (1964) *Op. cit.*

60. Thompson, C. J. S. (1928). *The Quacks of Old London.* p. 87. London: Brentano.

61. *Ibid.*, pp. 126–128.

62. *Ibid.*, p. 131.

63. *Ibid.*, p. 49.

64. *Ibid.*, p. 50.

65. *Ibid.*, pp. 53–54.

66. *Ibid.*, p. 258.

Chapter 10. *Infectious diseases*

1. Phillips, E. D. (1973). *Greek Medicine*, p. 66 London: Thames & Hudson.

2. Ross, R. (1898). Pigmented cells in mosquitos. *Brit. med. J.* **i**, 550–551.

3. Spencer, H. R. (1929). *Medicine in the Days of Shakespeare*, p. 23. London: John Bale, Sons & Danielsson.

4. Anon. (1987). Tabor's (or Talbor's) cure of the ague. *J. roy. Coll. Physns. London*, **21**, 66.

5. Doggett, M. (1682). *Her Booke of Receits*, p. 64. London: British Library, Sloane MS 27466.

6. Grey, E. (1653). *A Choice Mannuall or Rare and Select Secrets in Physick*, p. 139. London: Shears.

7. Sowerby, L. (1652). *The Ladies Dispensatory*, pp. 184, 185. London: Calvert.

8. Creighton, C. (1891). *A History of Epidemics in Britain*, vol. 1, p. 419. Cambridge: Cambridge University Press.

9. *Ibid.*, p. 429.

10. Barrough, P. (1617). *The Method of Physick*, p. 380. London: Field.

11. Bruel, W. (1630). *Praxis medicinae or The Physicians Practice*, pp. 392–396. London: Sheares.

12. Beier, L. M. (1987). *Sufferers and Healers*, pp. 89–91. London: Routledge & Kegan Paul.

13. Binns, J. (N. D.) *Surgical casebook*, p. 172. London: British Library, Sloane MS 153.

14. Garrison, F. H. (1929). *An Introduction to the History of Medicine*, 4th edn., p. 579. Philadelphia: Saunders.

15. Willis, T. (1684). *Practice of Physick*, translated by Pordage, S., IX(2), p. 28. London: Dring, Harper & Leigh.

16. Hippocrates (N. D.) *The Genuine*

Works of Hippocrates, translated by Adams, F. (1849), p. 294. Baltimore: Williams & Wilkins.

17. Rubin, S. (1974). *Medieval English Medicine*, p. 36. Newton Abbott: David & Charles.

18. Copeman, W. S. C. (1960). *Doctors and Disease in Tudor Times*, p. 134. London: Dawson.

19. Cassedy, J. H. (1974). Medicine and the rise of statistics. In Debus, A. G. (ed.) *Medicine in Seventeenth Century England*, pp. 283–312. Berkeley: University of California.

20. Sydenham, T. (1722). *The Whole Works of that Excellent Practical Physician, Dr Thomas Sydenham*, translated by Pechey, J., p. 193. London: Butterworth & Clay.

21. Wiseman, R. (1676). *Severall Chirurgicall Treatises*, p. 245. London: Royston & Took.

22. *Ibid.*, p. 329.

23. Guthrie, D. (1945). *A History of Medicine*, p. 28. Edinburgh: Nelson.

24. Yersin, A. (1894). La peste bubonique à Hong-Kong. *Ann. de l'Inst. Pasteur*, **8**, 662–667.

25. Kitisato, S. (1894). The bacillus of bubonic plague. *Lancet*, **ii**, 428–430.

26. Hirst, L. F. (1933). *The Conquest of Plague*, p. 246. Oxford: Clarendon.

27. *Ibid.*, p. 184.

28. *Ibid.*, p. 441.

29. Stow, J. (1605). *The Annales or Generall Chronicle of England*, continued and augmented to 1614 by Howes, E. (1615), p. 508. London: Adams.

30. Wilson, F. P. (1927). *The Plague in Shakespeare's London*, p. 61. London: Oxford University Press.

31. *Ibid.*, pp. 56–57.

32. *Ibid.*, pp. 34–35.

33. Shrewsbury, J. F. D. (1970). *A History of Bubonic Plague in the British Isles*, p. 267. Cambridge: Cambridge University Press.

34. Dekker, T. (1603). *The Wonderfull Yeare*, sig. D, C3. London: Creede.

35. Slack, P. (1985). *The Impact of Plague in Tudor and Stuart England*, p. 151. London: Routledge & Kegan Paul.

36. Creighton, C. (1891). *Op. cit.*, p. 509.

37. Slack, P. (1985). *Op. cit.*, p. 151.

38. Shrewsbury, J. F. D. (1970). *Op. cit.*, p. 332.

39. Defoe, D. (1722). *A Journal of the Plague Year*, with foreword by Plumb, J. H. (1960), p. 28. New York: Signet.

40. Creighton, C. (1891). *Op. cit.*, p. 660.

41. Bell, W. G. (1924). *The Great Plague of London in 1665*, 2nd edn. 1951, p. 18. London: Lane.

42. Pepys, S. (1665). *Diary*, ed. by Teeble, H. H. (1927), pp. 137ff. London: Harrap.

43. Vincent, T. (1667). *Gods Terrible Voice in the City*, reprint with preface by Evans, J. (1672), p. 42. London: Clark.

44. Evelyn, J. (1665). *Diary*, ed. by Francis, P. (1963), p. 146. London: Folio Society.

45. Austin, W. (1666). *Op. cit.*, p. 27

46. Shrewsbury, J. F. D. (1970). *Op. cit.*, p. 463.

47. Creighton, C. (1891). *Op. cit.*, pp. 687–689.

48. *Ibid.*, pp. 689–690.
49. Phaire, T. (1545). *The Boke of Chyldren*, reprinted 1955, p. 56. Edinburgh: Livingstone.
50. Creighton, C. (1894). *A History of Epidemics in Britain*, vol. 2, p. 438. Cambridge: Cambridge University Press.
51. Harvey, G. (1696). *A Treatise of the Small-pox and Measles*, p. 29. London: Freeman.
52. Sydenham, T. (1722). *Op. cit.*, pp. 79–82.
53. Gale, A. H. (1959). *Epidemic Diseases*, p. 59. Harmondsworth: Penguin.
54. Carmichael, A. G. & Silverstein, A. M. (1987). Smallpox in Europe before the seventeenth century: virulent killer or benign disease? *J. Hist. Med.* **42**, 147–168.
55. Brown, H. F. (ed.) (1900). *Calendar of State Papers, Venetian*, vol. 10 (1603–1607), p. 281. London: H. M. Stationery Office.
56. Wilson, F. P. (1927). *Op. cit.*, pp. 120–124.
57. Creighton, C. (1891). *Op. cit.*, pp. 465–466.
58. Creighton, C. (1894). *Op. cit.*, p. 456.
59. *Ibid.*, p. 458.
60. Harris, W. (1689). *A Treatise of the Acute Diseases of Infants*, translated by Martin, J. (1742), p. 106. London: Astley.
61. Creighton, C. (1894). *Op. cit.*, p. 451.
62. Harvey, G. (1696). *Op. cit.*, p. 120.
63. *Ibid.*, p. 161.
64. *Ibid.*, p. 179.
65. Creighton, C. (1891). Op. cit., p. 448.
66. Harvey, G. (1696). *Op. cit.*, p. 99.
67. Gale, A. H. (1959). *Op. cit.*, pp. 99–100.
68. Creighton, C. (1894). *Op. cit.*, pp. 636–637.
69. Poynter, F. N. L. & Bishop, J. W. (1951). *A Seventeenth Century Doctor and his Patients: John Symcotts (1592?–1662)*, p. 57. Streatly: Bedfordshire Historical Records Society.
70. Sydenham, T. (1722). *Op. cit.*, pp. 132–133.
71. Boorde, A. (1547). *The Breviary of Helthe*, p. 57. London: Middleton.
72. Poynter, F. N. L. & Bishop, J. W. (1951). *Op. cit.*, p. 57.
73. Sydenham, T. (1722). *Op. cit.*, p. 134.
74. Greenwood, M. (1935). *Epidemics and Crowd-Diseases*, p. 174. London: Williams & Norgate.
75. Risse, G. B. (1979). Epidemics and medicine: the influence of disease on medical thought and practice. Bull. Hist. Med. **53** 505–519.
76. Creighton, C. (1891). *Op. cit.*, pp. 375–386.
77. *Ibid.*, p. 547.
78. Gale, A. H. (1959). *Op. cit.*, p. 73.
79. Creighton, C. (1891). *Op. cit.*, p. 552.
80. Creighton, C. (1894). *Op. cit.*, pp. 22–32, 44.
81. *Ibid.*, p. 47.
82. Sydenham, T. (1722). *Op. cit.*, pp. 410–411.
83. Willis, T. (1684). *Op. cit.*, VIII, pp. 46–47.
84. Sydenham, T (1722). *Op. cit.*, p. 414.

85. Willis, T. (1684). *Op. cit.*, VIII, p. 52.
86. *Ibid.*, II, p. 79.
87. Sydenham, T. (1722). *Op. cit.*, pp. 434–438.
88. Barbette, P. (1675). *The Practice of the Most Successful Physitian Paul Barbette*, edited by Deckers, F., p. 188. London: Brome.
89. Sydenham, T. (1722). *Op. cit.*, p. 117.
90. Bruel, W. (1630). *Op. cit.*, p. 300.
91. Grey, E. (1653). *Op. cit.*, p. 138.
92. Creighton, C. (1894). *Op. cit.*, pp. 750–752.
93. Harris, W. (1689). *Op. cit.*, p. 55.
94. *Ibid.*, p. 96.
95. Pechey, J. (1697). *A General Treatise of the Diseases of Infants and Children*, pp. 17, 104. London: Wellington.
96. Major, R. H. (1954). *A History of Medicine*, p. 633. Oxford: Blackwell.

97. Creighton, C. (1894). *Op, cit.*, pp. 313, 326–329, 335–338.
98. Smith, W., Andrewes, C. H.& Laidlow, P. P. (1933). A virus obtained from influenza patients. Lancet. **ii**, 66–68.
99. Gale, A. H. (1959). *Op. cit.*, p. 43.
100. Sydenham, T. (1722). *Op. cit.*, pp. 173–174.
101. *Ibid.*, p. 178.
102. Gale, A. H. (1959). *Op. cit.*, p. 49
103. Creighton, C. (1894). *Op. cit.*, p. 682.
104. *Ibid.*, p. 666.
105. Sydenham, T. (1722). *Op. cit.*, p. 235
106. Gale, A. H. (1959). *Op. cit.*, p. 104.
107. Radbill, S. L. (1974). Pediatrics. In Debus A. G. (ed.) *Medicine in Seventeenth Century England*, pp. 237–282. Berkeley: University of California.
108. *Idem.*

Chapter 11. The legacy of the seventeenth century

1. Singer, C. (1941). *A Short History of Science*, p. 234. Oxford: Clarendon.
2. King, L. S. (1958). *The Medical World of the Eighteenth Century*, p. 100. Chicago: University of Chicago Press.
3. *Ibid.*, p. 123.
4. Garrison, F. H. (1929). *An Introduction to the History of Medicine*, 4th edn., pp. 578–579. Philadelphia: Saunders.
5. *Ibid.*, p. 581.
6. King, L. S. (1958), *Op. cit.*, p. 133.
7. *Ibid.*, p. 18.

8. Porter, R. (1987). *Disease, Medicine and Society in England 1550–1860*, p. 19. Basingstoke: Macmillan.
9. Garrison, F. H. (1929). *Op. cit.*, p. 474.
10. *Ibid.*, p. 656.
11. Copeman, W. S. C. (1967). *The Worshipful Society of Apothecaries of London*, p. 64. London: Pergamon.
12. *Ibid.*, p. 66.
13. Garrison, F. H. (1929). *Op. cit.*, p. 343.
14. *Ibid.*, p. 544.
15. *Ibid.*, pp. 344–345.

16. *Ibid.*, p. 338.
17. *Ibid.*, p. 340.
18. Eccles, A. (1982). *Obstetrics and Gynaecology in Tudor and Stuart England*, p. 115. London: Croom Helm.
19. King, L. S. (1958). *Op. cit.*, p. 34.
20. *Ibid.*, p. 40.
21. *Ibid.*, p. 48.
22. *Ibid.*, p. 51.
23. Clark, G. (1966). *A History of the Royal College of Physicians of London*, vol. 2, p. 517. Oxford: Clarendon.
24. Garrison, F. H. (1929). *Op. cit.*, p. 239.
25. Copeman, W. S. C. (1967). *Op. cit.*, pp. 66–69.
26. Billings, J. S. (1970). *The History and Literature of Surgery*, p. 70. New York: Argosy.
27. *Ibid.*, p. 71.
28. Cartwright, F. F. (1977). *A Social History of Medicine*, p. 37. London: Longmans.
29. Comrie, J. D. (1932). *History of Scottish Medicine*, p. 298. London: Baillière, Tindall & Cox.
30. Cartwright, F. F. (1977). *Op. cit.*, pp. 101, 104–105.
31. *Ibid.*, p. 112.

Index